21ST CENTURY ROCK

GUITAR TAB EDITION

PUBLISHED BY
WISE PUBLICATIONS,
8/9 FRITH STREET,
LONDON W1D 3JB, ENGLAND.

EXCLUSIVE DISTRIBUTORS:
MUSIC SALES LIMITED
DISTRIBUTION CENTRE,
NEWMARKET ROAD, BURY ST EDMUNDS,
SUFFOLK, IP33 3YB, ENGLAND.
MUSIC SALES PTY LIMITED
120 ROTHSCHILD AVENUE, ROSEBERY,
NSW 2018, AUSTRALIA.

ORDER NO. AM89484
ISBN 0-7119-3035-X
THIS BOOK © COPYRIGHT 2004
BY WISE PUBLICATIONS.

UNAUTHORISED REPRODUCTION OF ANY
PART OF THIS PUBLICATION BY
ANY MEANS INCLUDING PHOTOCOPYING IS
AN INFRINGEMENT OF COPYRIGHT.

COMPILED BY NICK CRISPIN.
MUSIC ARRANGED BY MATT COWE.
MUSIC PROCESSED BY PAUL EWERS MUSIC DESIGN.

COVER DESIGN BY FRESH LEMON.
PRINTED IN MALTA BY INTERPRINT LIMITED.

YOUR GUARANTEE OF QUALITY:
AS PUBLISHERS, WE STRIVE TO PRODUCE EVERY
BOOK TO THE HIGHEST COMMERCIAL STANDARDS.
THE MUSIC HAS BEEN FRESHLY ENGRAVED AND
THE BOOK HAS BEEN CAREFULLY DESIGNED
TO MINIMISE AWKWARD PAGE TURNS AND TO
MAKE PLAYING FROM IT A REAL PLEASURE.
PARTICULAR CARE HAS BEEN GIVEN TO
SPECIFYING ACID-FREE, NEUTRAL-SIZED
PAPER MADE FROM PULPS WHICH HAVE
NOT BEEN ELEMENTAL CHLORINE BLEACHED.
THIS PULP IS FROM FARMED SUSTAINABLE
FORESTS AND WAS PRODUCED WITH
SPECIAL REGARD FOR THE ENVIRONMENT.
THROUGHOUT, THE PRINTING AND BINDING HAVE
BEEN PLANNED TO ENSURE A STURDY,
ATTRACTIVE PUBLICATION WHICH
SHOULD GIVE YEARS OF ENJOYMENT.
IF YOUR COPY FAILS TO MEET OUR HIGH STANDARDS,
PLEASE INFORM US AND WE WILL GLADLY REPLACE IT.

WWW.MUSICSALES.COM

GW00643055

WISE PUBLICATIONS
part of The Music Sales Group

LONDON / NEW YORK / PARIS / SYDNEY / COPENHAGEN / BERLIN / MADRID / TOKYO

GUITAR TABLATURE EXPLAINED
GUITAR MUSIC CAN BE NOTATED IN THREE DIFFERENT WAYS: ON A MUSICAL STAVE, IN TABLATURE AND IN RHYTHM SLASHES

RHYTHM SLASHES are written above the stave. Strum chords in the rhythm indicated. Round noteheads indicate single notes.

THE MUSICAL STAVE shows pitches and rhythms and is divided by lines into bars. Pitches are named after the first seven letters of the alphabet.

TABLATURE graphically represents the guitar fingerboard. Each horizontal line represents a string, and each number represents a fret.

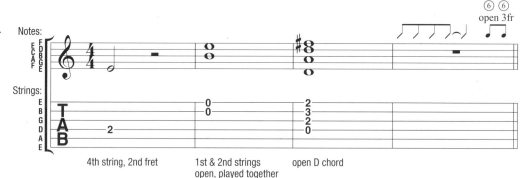

4th string, 2nd fret   1st & 2nd strings open, played together   open D chord

DEFINITIONS FOR SPECIAL GUITAR NOTATION

SEMI-TONE BEND: Strike the note and bend up a semi-tone (1/2 step).

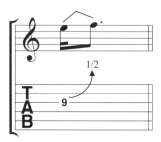

WHOLE-TONE BEND: Strike the note and bend up a whole-tone (whole step).

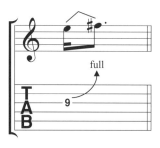

GRACE NOTE BEND: Strike the note and bend as indicated. Play the first note as quickly as possible.

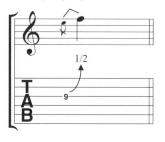

QUARTER-TONE BEND: Strike the note and bend up a 1/4 step.

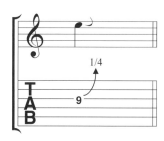

BEND & RELEASE: Strike the note and bend up as indicated, then release back to the original note.

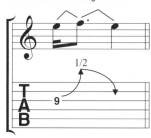

COMPOUND BEND & RELEASE: Strike the note and bend up and down in the rhythm indicated.

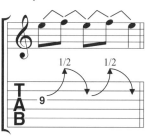

PRE-BEND: Bend the note as indicated, then strike it.

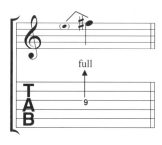

PRE-BEND & RELEASE: Bend the note as indicated. Strike it and release the note back to the original pitch.

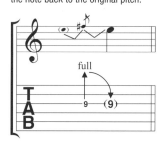

UNISON BEND: Strike the two notes simultaneously and bend the lower note up to the pitch of the higher.

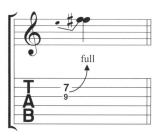

BEND & RESTRIKE: Strike the note and bend as indicated then restrike the string where the symbol occurs.

BEND, HOLD AND RELEASE: Same as bend and release but hold the bend for the duration of the tie.

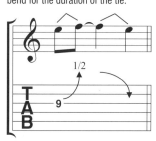

BEND AND TAP: Bend the note as indicated and tap the higher fret while still holding the bend.

VIBRATO: The string is vibrated by rapidly bending and releasing the note with the fretting hand.

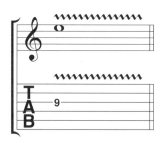

HAMMER-ON: Strike the first note with one finger, then sound the second note (on the same string) with another finger by fretting it without picking.

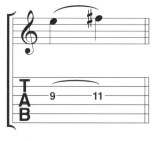

PULL-OFF: Place both fingers on the notes to be sounded, strike the first note and without picking, pull the finger off to sound the second note.

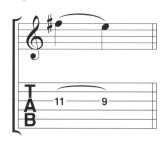

LEGATO SLIDE (GLISS): Strike the first note and then slide the same fret-hand finger up or down to the second note. The second note is not struck.

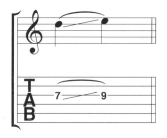

NOTE: The speed of any bend is indicated by the music notation and tempo.

SHIFT SLIDE (GLISS & RESTRIKE): Same as legato slide, except the second note is struck.

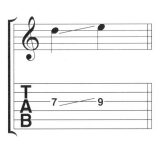

TRILL: Very rapidly alternate between the notes indicated by continuously hammering on and pulling off.

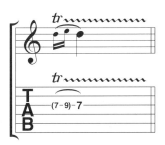

TAPPING: Hammer ("tap") the fret indicated with the pick-hand index or middle finger and pull off to the note fretted by the fret hand.

PICK SCRAPE: The edge of the pick is rubbed down (or up) the string, producing a scratchy sound.

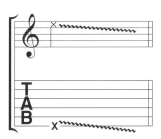

MUFFLED STRINGS: A percussive sound is produced by laying the fret hand across the string(s) without depressing, and striking them with the pick hand.

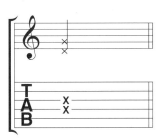

NATURAL HARMONIC: Strike the note while the fret-hand lightly touches the string directly over the fret indicated.

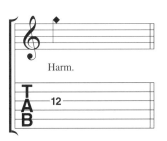

PINCH HARMONIC: The note is fretted normally and a harmonic is produced by adding the edge of the thumb or the tip of the index finger of the pick hand to the normal pick attack.

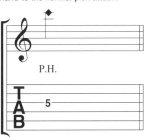

HARP HARMONIC: The note is fretted normally and a harmonic is produced by gently resting the pick hand's index finger directly above the indicated fret (in brackets) while plucking the appropriate string.

PALM MUTING: The note is partially muted by the pick hand lightly touching the string(s) just before the bridge.

RAKE: Drag the pick across the strings indicated with a single motion.

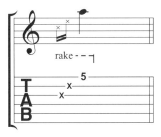

TREMOLO PICKING: The note is picked as rapidly and continuously as possible.

ARPEGGIATE: Play the notes of the chord indicated by quickly rolling them from bottom to top.

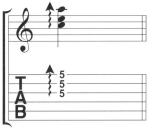

SWEEP PICKING: Rhythmic downstroke and/or upstroke motion across the strings.

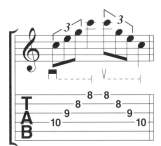

VIBRATO DIVE BAR AND RETURN: The pitch of the note or chord is dropped a specific number of steps (in rhythm) then returned to the original pitch.

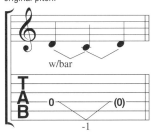

VIBRATO BAR SCOOP: Depress the bar just before striking the note, then quickly release the bar.

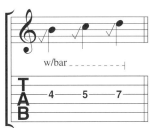

VIBRATO BAR DIP: Strike the note and then immediately drop a specific number of steps, then release back to the original pitch.

ADDITIONAL MUSICAL DEFINITIONS

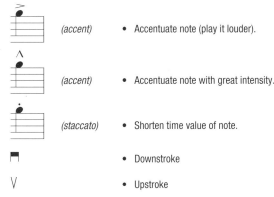	(accent)	• Accentuate note (play it louder).
	(accent)	• Accentuate note with great intensity.
	(staccato)	• Shorten time value of note.
■		• Downstroke
V		• Upstroke

D.%. al Coda	• Go back to the sign (%), then play until the bar marked **To Coda** ⊕ then skip to the section marked ⊕ **Coda**.
D.C. al Fine	• Go back to the beginning of the song and play until the bar marked **Fine**.
tacet	• Instrument is silent (drops out).
	• Repeat bars between signs.
1. 2.	• When a repeated section has different endings, play the first ending only the first time and the second ending only the second time.

NOTE: Tablature numbers in brackets mean:
1. The note is sustained, but a new articulation (such as hammer on or slide) begins.
2. A note may be fretted but not necessarily played.

BEHIND BLUE EYES

WORDS & MUSIC BY PETE TOWNSHEND

dreams _____ they aren't as emp - ty as my

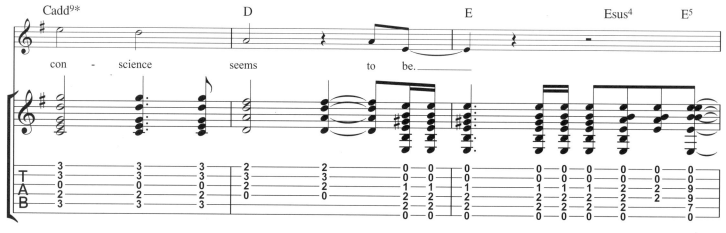

con - science seems to be. ____

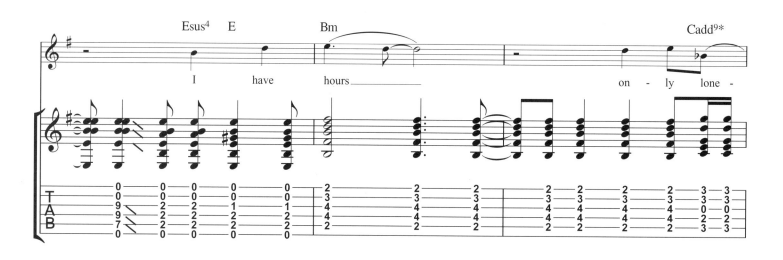

I have hours _____ on - ly lone -

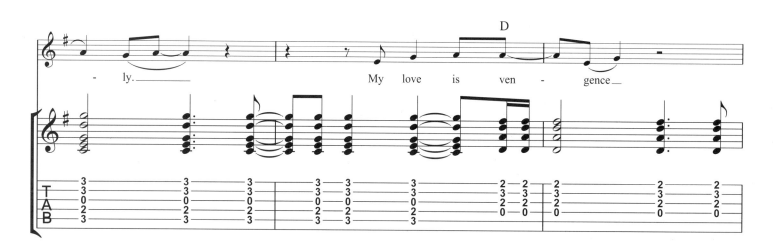

- ly. _____ My love is ven - gence

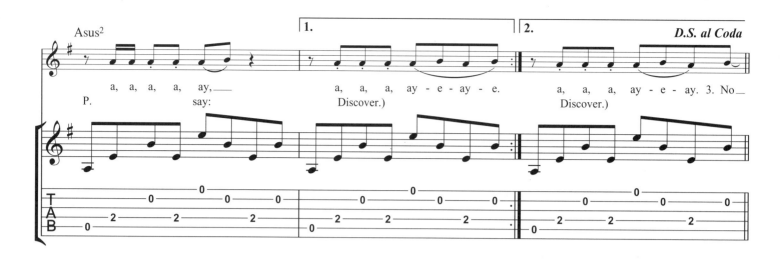

COCHISE

WORDS BY CHRIS CORNELL

MUSIC BY CHRIS CORNELL, TIM COMMERFORD, TOM MORELLO & BRAD WILK

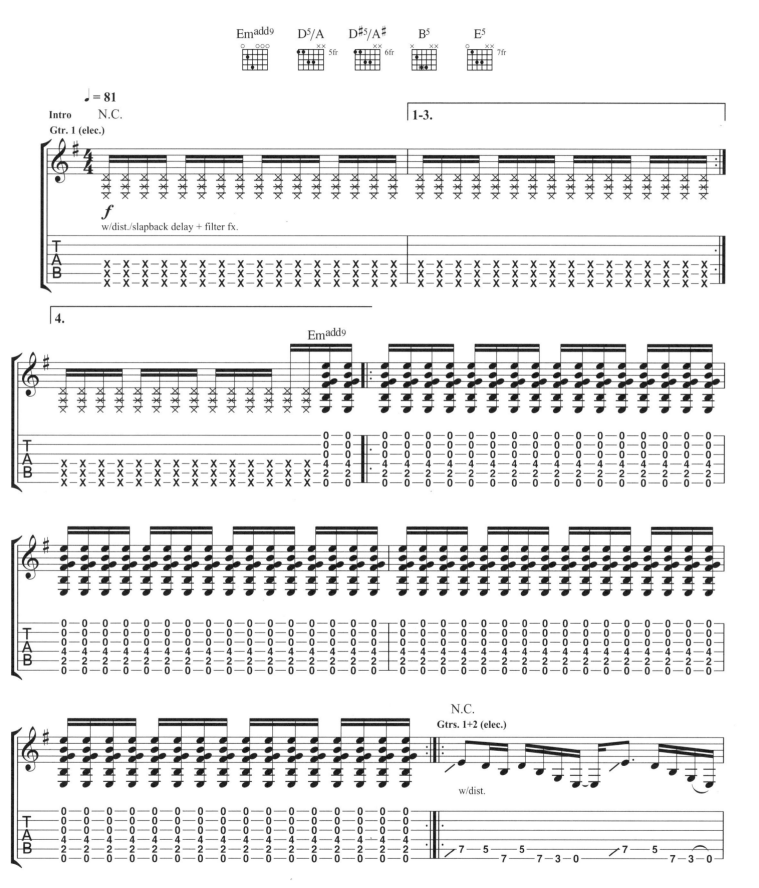

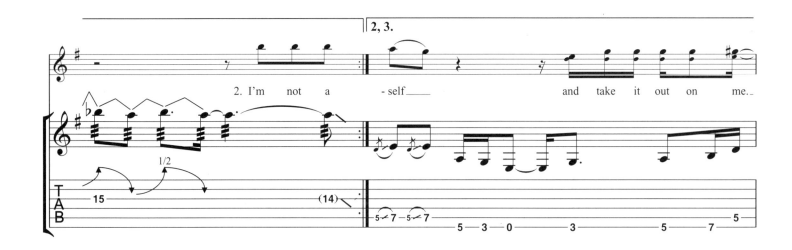

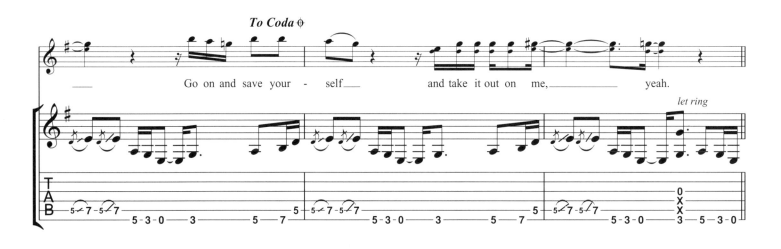

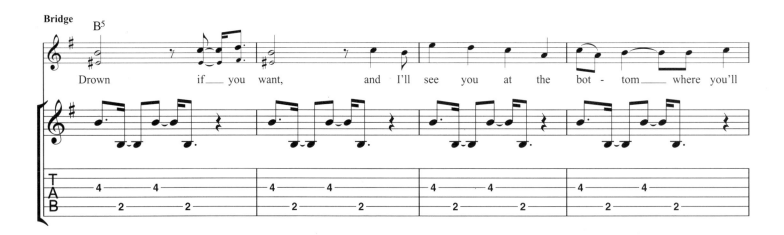

CRAWL HOME

WORDS & MUSIC BY JOSH HOMME, ALAIN JOHANNES, POLLY JEAN HARVEY, JOEY CASTILLO & JEORDIE WHITE

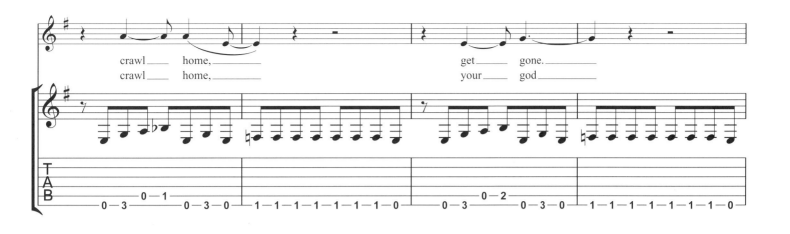

crawl___ home,___ get___ gone.___
crawl___ home,___ your___ god___

Your___ love___ is e - vil,___
is e - vil,___ I'm lone - some,___

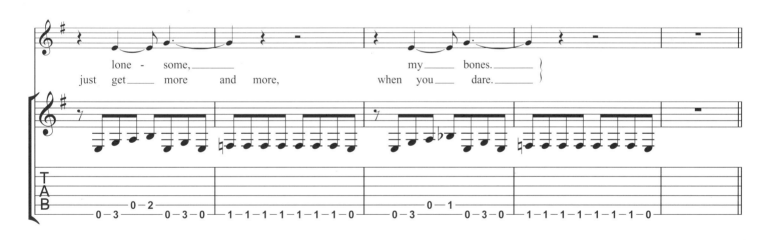

lone - some,___ my___ bones.___
just get___ more and more, when you___ dare.___

Chorus

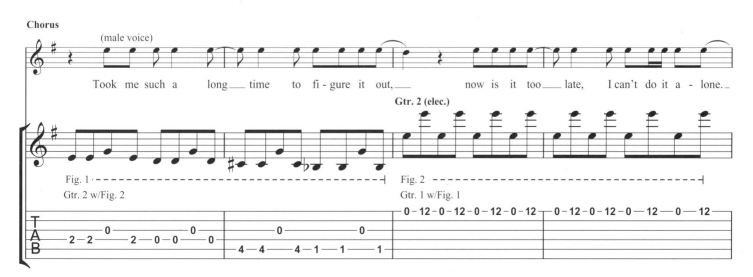

(male voice)

Took me such a long___ time to fi - gure it out,___ now is it too___ late, I can't do it a - lone.___

Gtr. 2 (elec.)

Fig. 1 ----------------------- Fig. 2 -----------------------

Gtr. 2 w/Fig. 2 Gtr. 1 w/Fig. 1

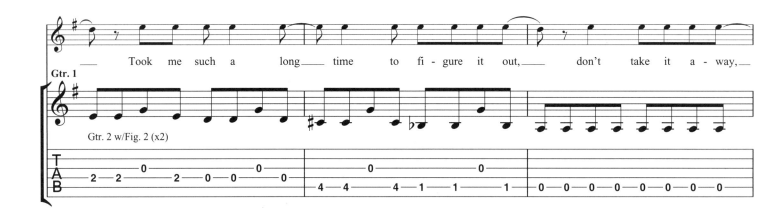

Took me such a long time to fi-gure it out, don't take it a-way,

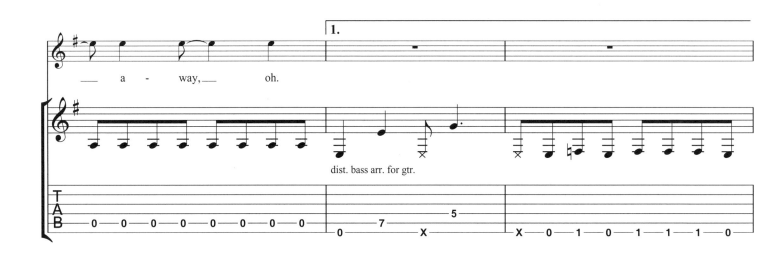

a - way, oh.

dist. bass arr. for gtr.

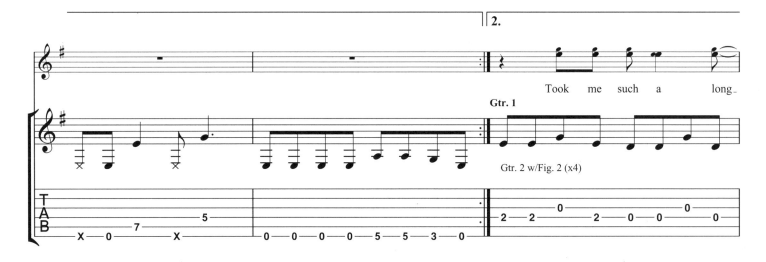

Took me such a long

Gtr. 1

Gtr. 2 w/Fig. 2 (x4)

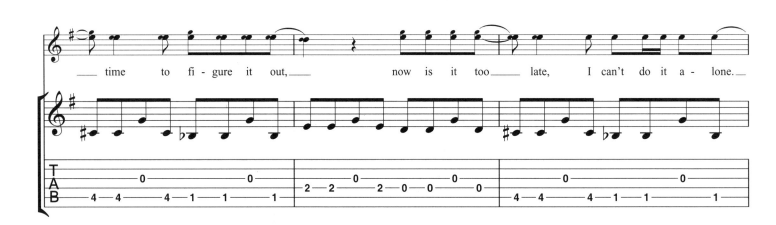

time to fi-gure it out, now is it too late, I can't do it a - lone.

Took me such a long time to fi-gure it out. Don't take me a-way, a-way, oh.

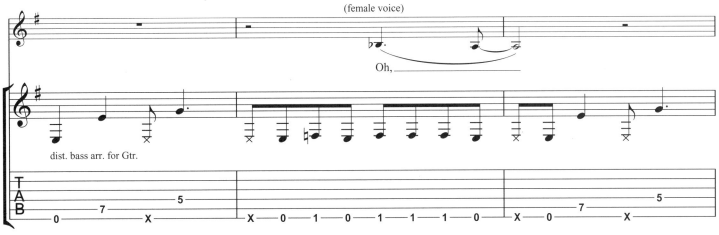

(female voice)

Oh,

dist. bass arr. for Gtr.

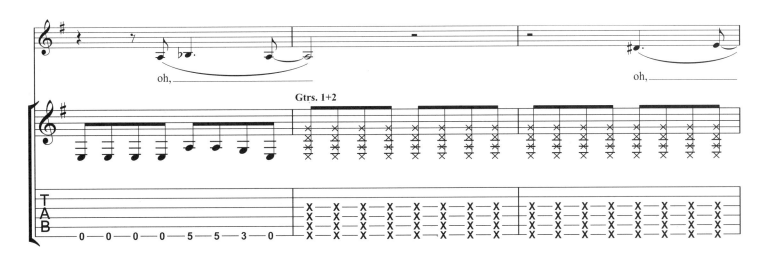

oh, oh,

Gtrs. 1+2

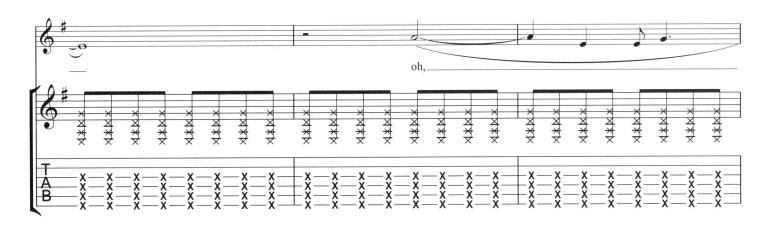

oh,

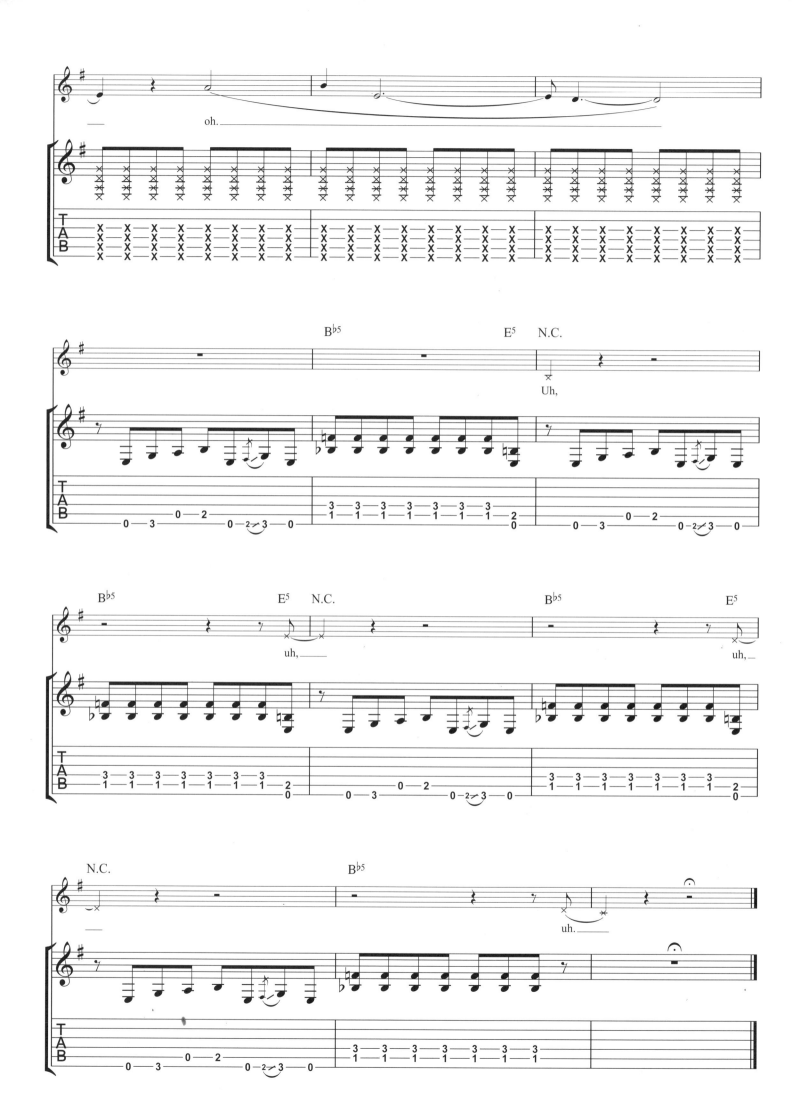

DUSTY

WORDS & MUSIC BY CALEB FOLLOWILL, NATHAN FOLLOWILL & ANGELO PETRAGLIA

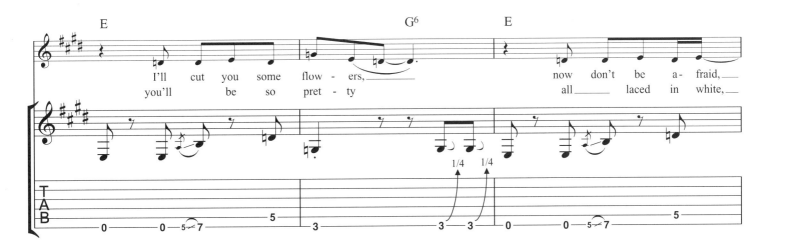

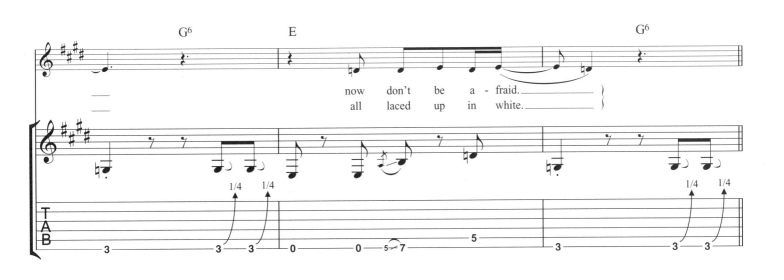

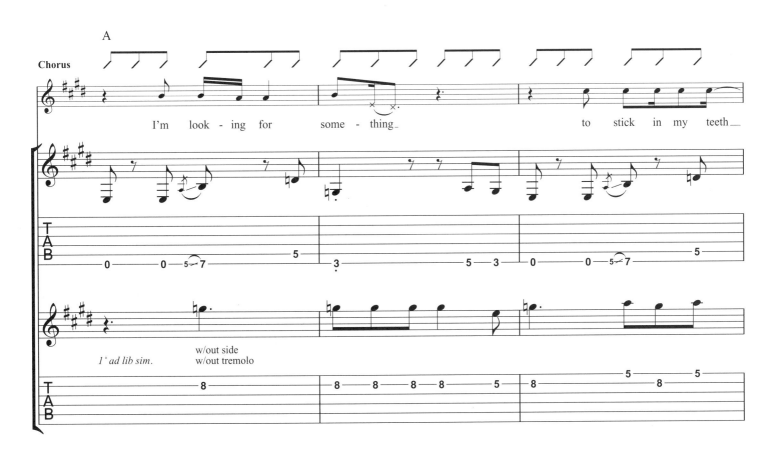

with - out a - ny cry - in'.

But I____ can't find

no place or no - thing, where thrills are cheap_____ and love is di - vine._____

I'm a - look - ing for some - thing   to stick in my

teeth___ with - out a - ny cry - ing.

But I___ can't find

no place or no__ thing, where thrills are cheap_____ and love is di - vine.__

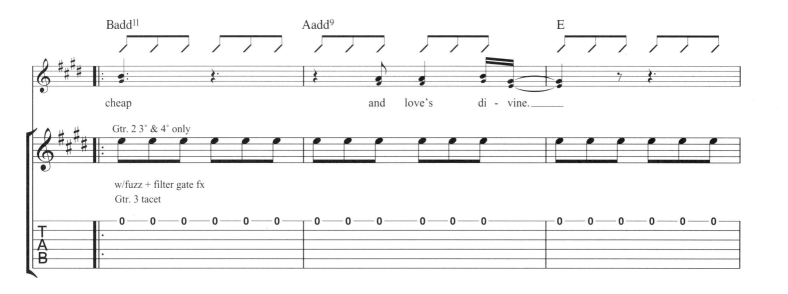

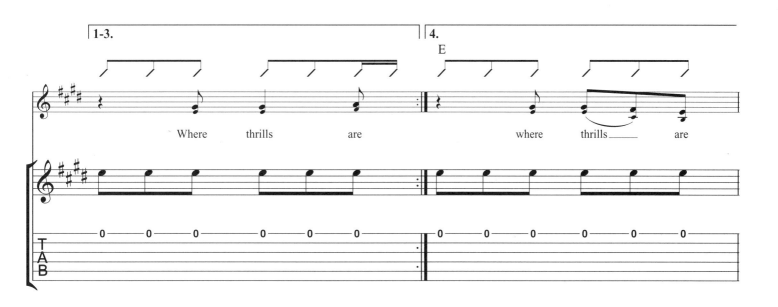

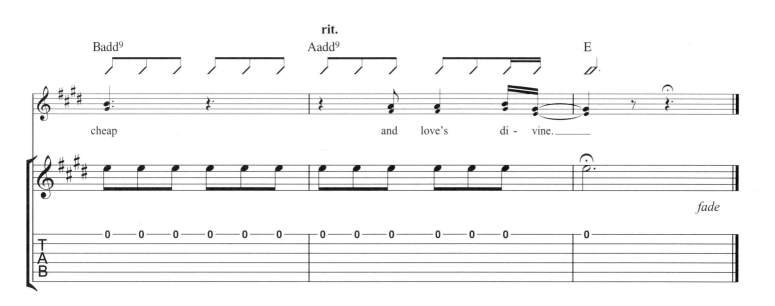

___ a-gain af-ter you came___ and went. How can you say___ you meant a-ny-thing diff-_

_-'rent to a-ny-one. Stand - ing a-lone__ on the street___ with a ci-gar-ette, on___

E⁵*   **B⁵**
Gtr. 1
cont. sim.
P.M.

___ the first night__ we met. Look to the past__ and re-mem - ber her smile____ and_

C♯⁵   **A⁵**   **E⁵***

_may - be to-night__ I can breathe__ for a while.___ I'm not in the seat,__ I think I'm_

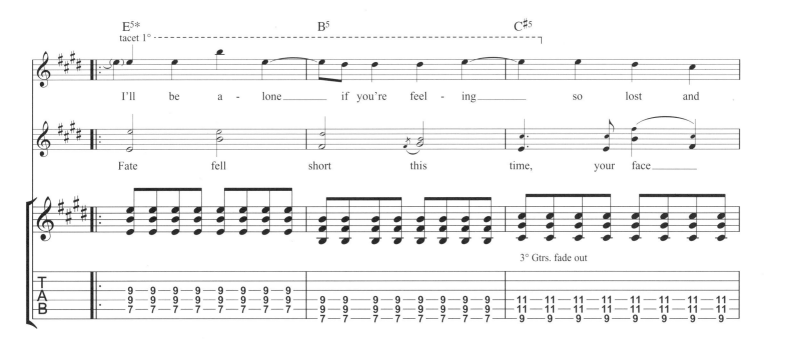

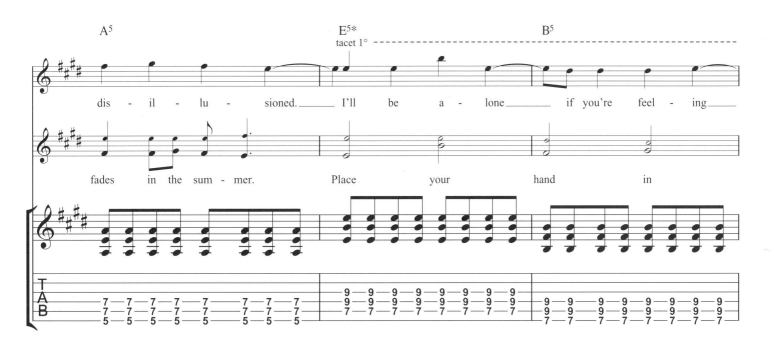

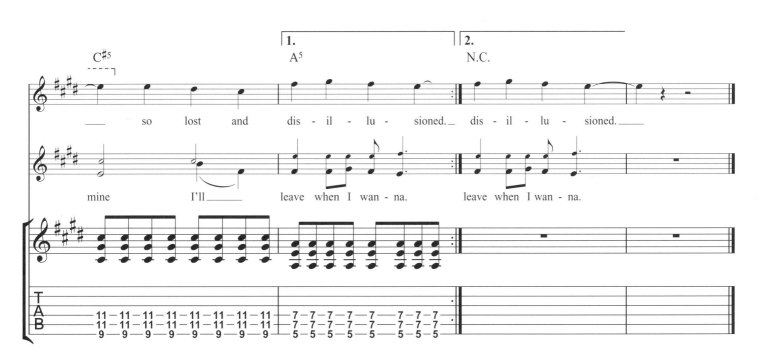

FIRST IT GIVETH

WORDS & MUSIC BY JOSH HOMME & NICK OLIVERI

you're ___ in me, ___ I can tell. ___

You're so cruel, ___ more ___ than me, ___ it is true.

Lo - yal too, ___ on - ly you, ___

up your sleeve.

I want some

(of) all of you, trick - ing me.

Chorus

First it gi - veth, then it ta - keth a - way.

Gtrs. 1+2

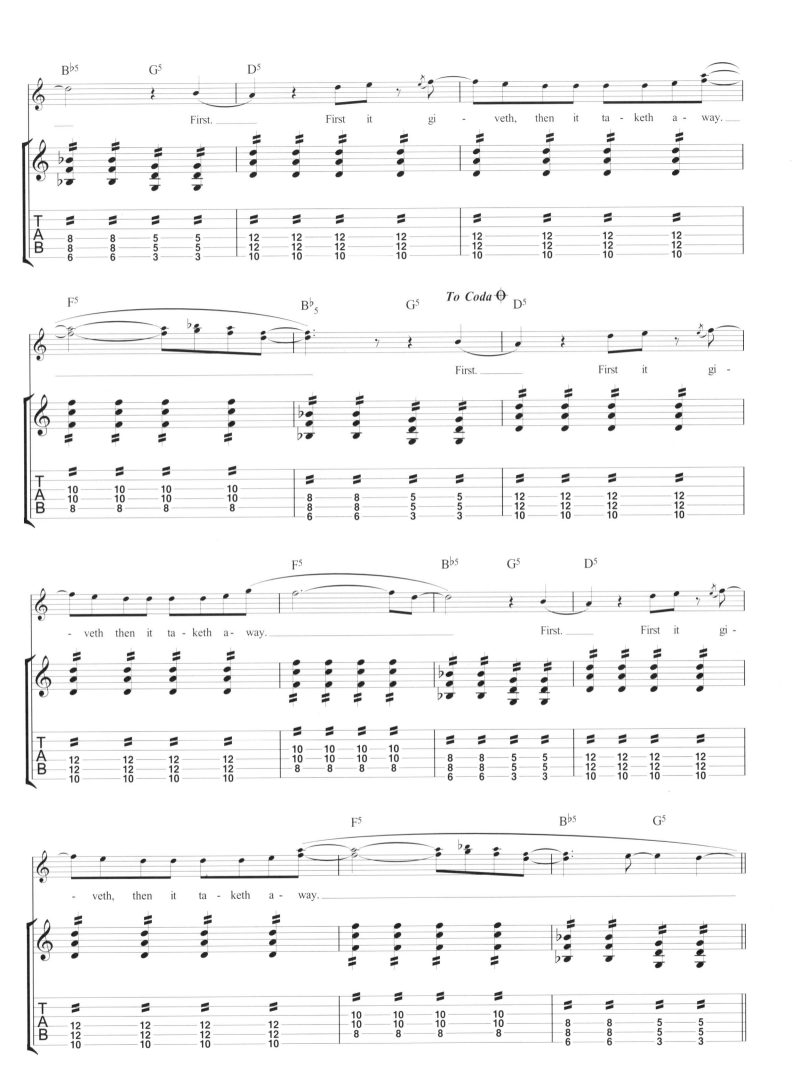

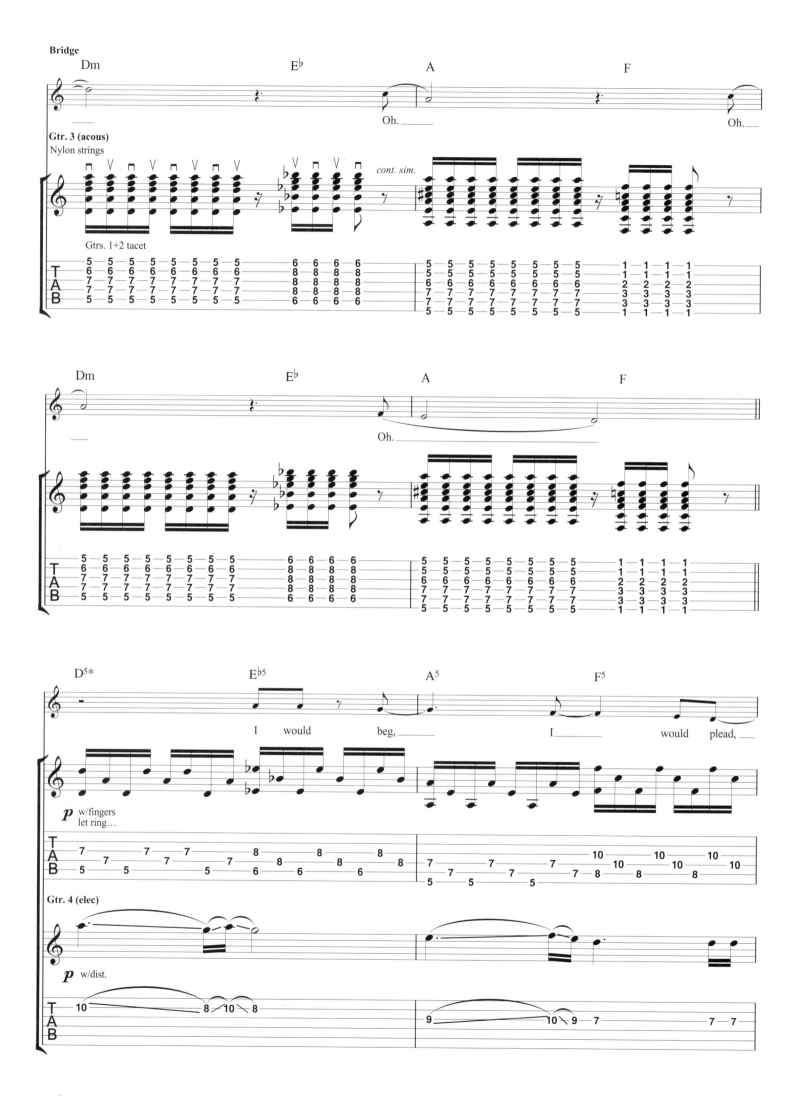

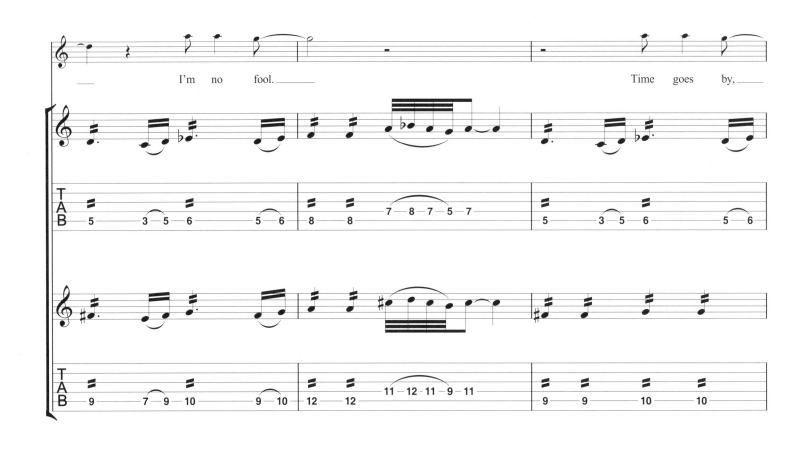

I'm no fool._____ Time goes by,_____

D.S. al Coda

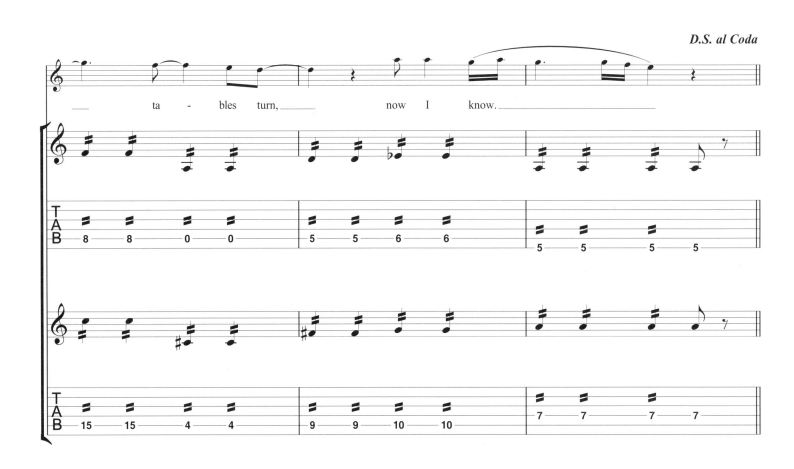

_____ ta - bles turn,_____ now I know._____

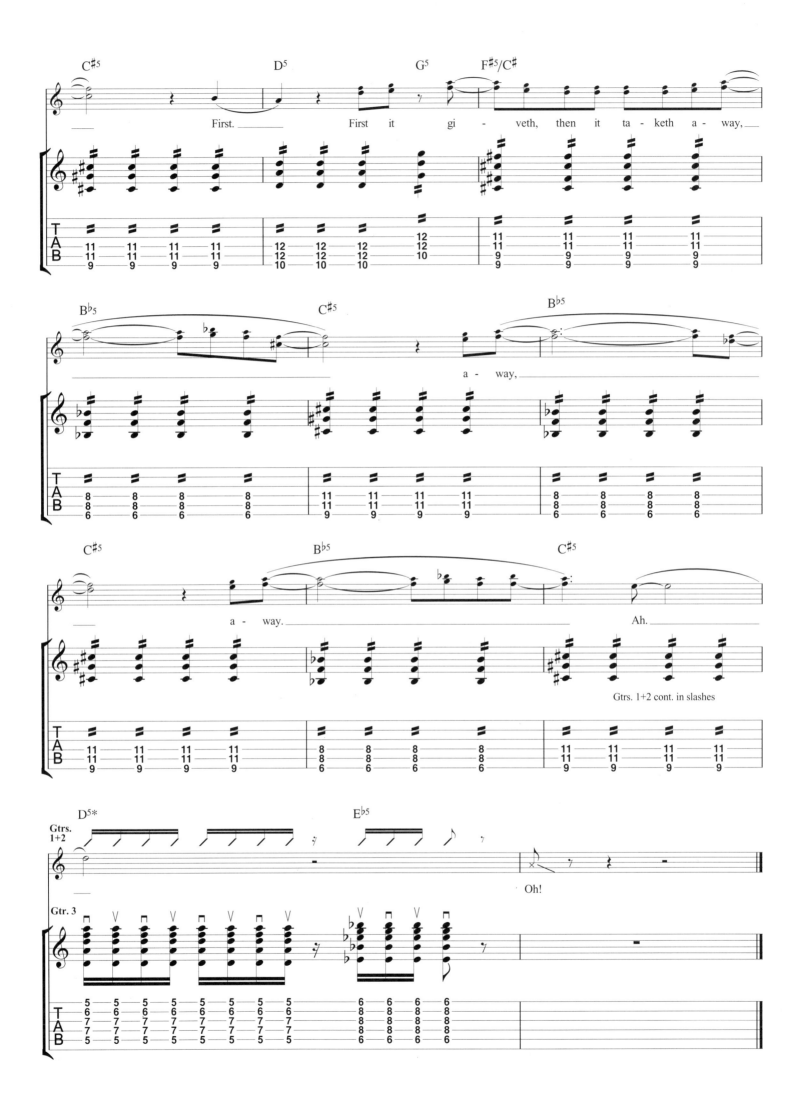

FUCK HER GENTLY

WORDS & MUSIC BY JACK BLACK & KYLE GASS

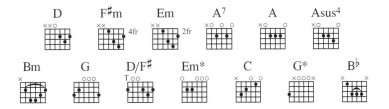

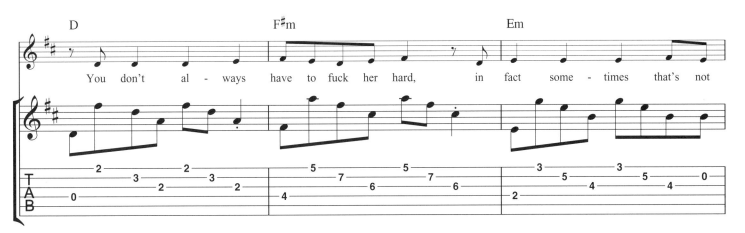

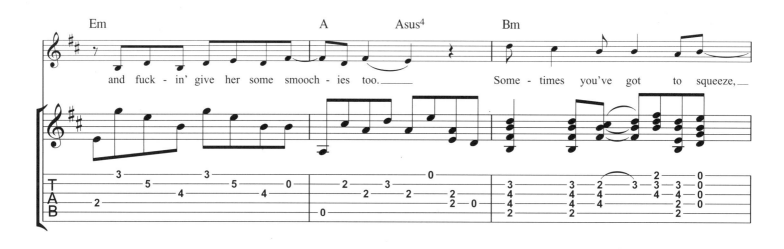

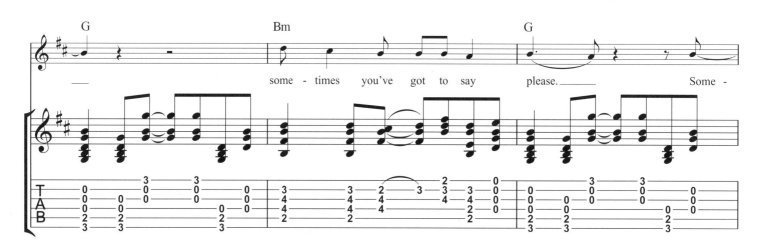

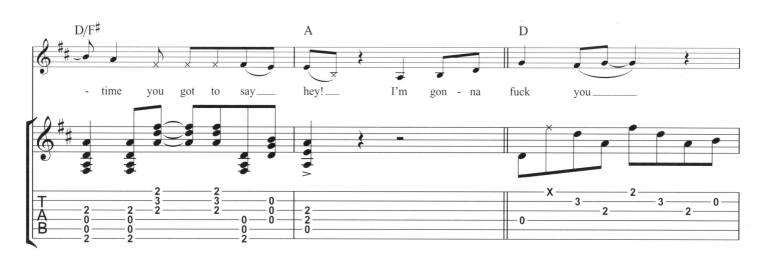

humpyou____ sweet-ly, I'm gon-na ball___ you dis-

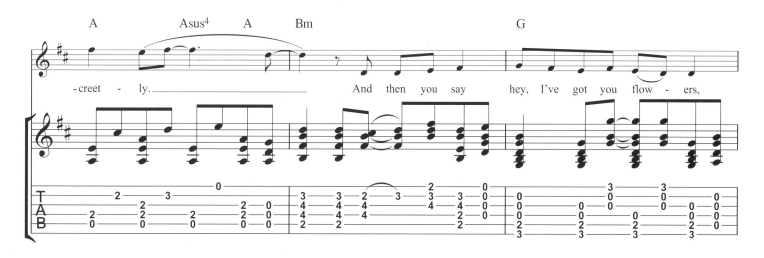

-creet - ly.____ And then you say hey, I've got you flow - ers,

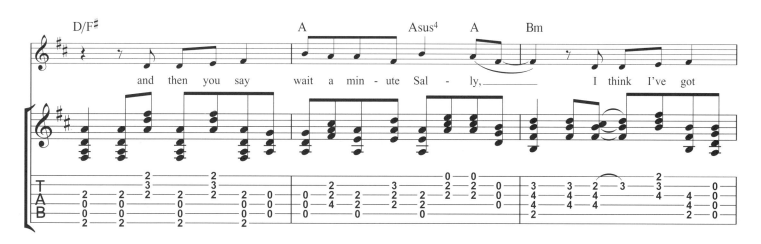

and then you say wait a min-ute Sal - ly,____ I think I've got

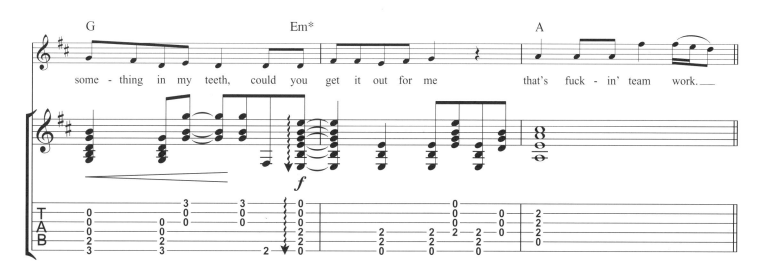

some - thing in my teeth, could you get it out for me that's fuck - in' team work.___

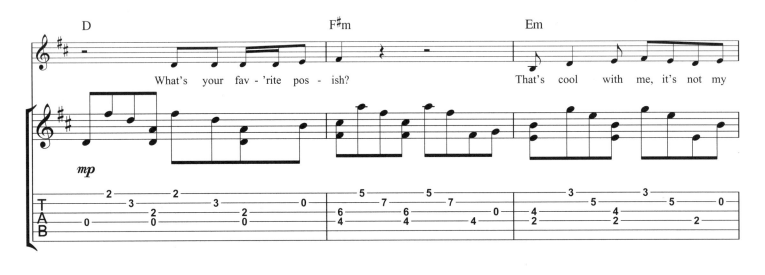

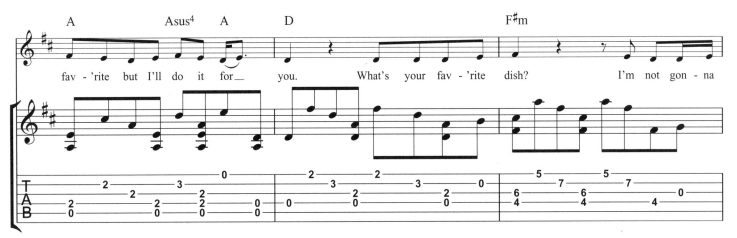

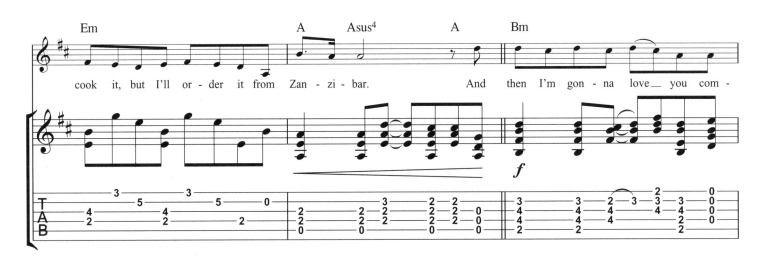

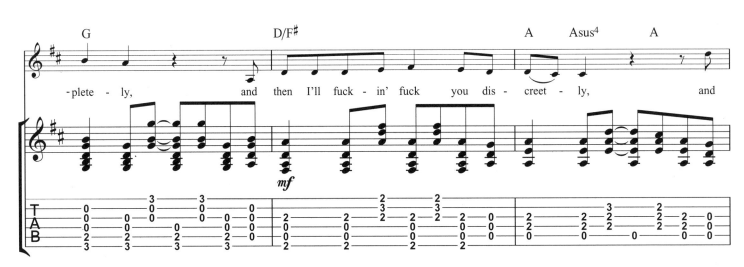

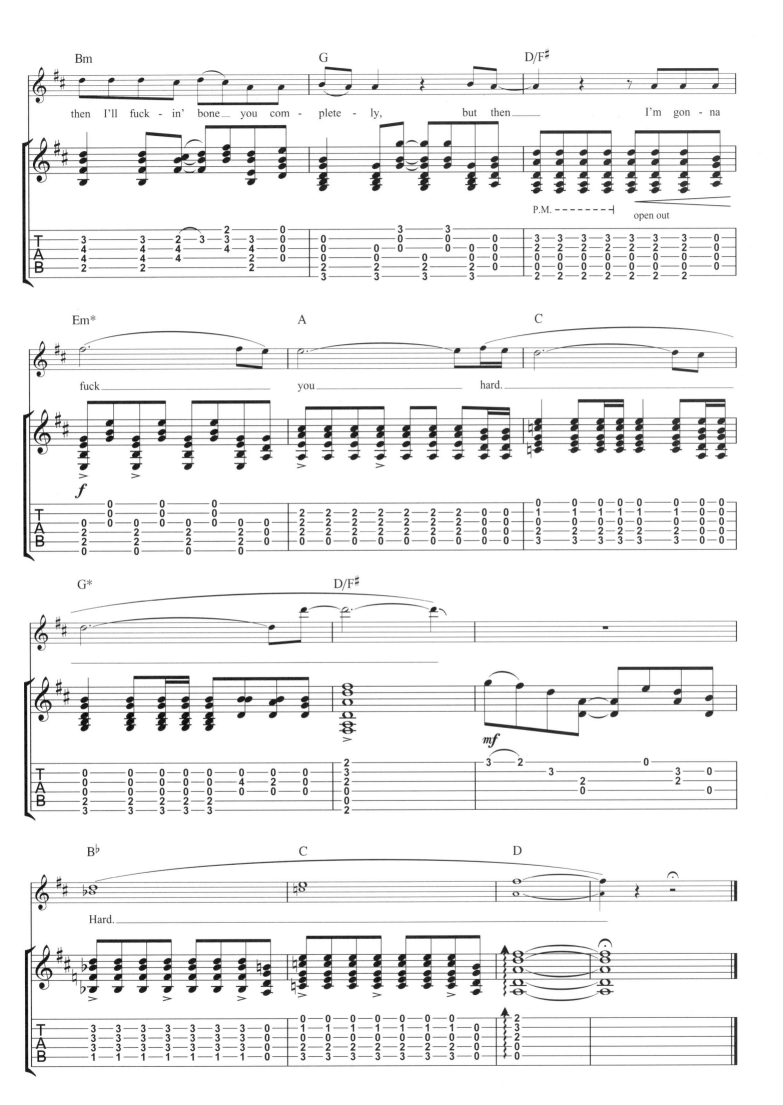

49

FRANTIC

WORDS & MUSIC BY JAMES HETFIELD, LARS ULRICH, KIRK HAMMETT & BOB ROCK

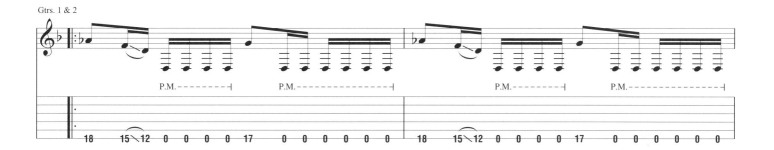

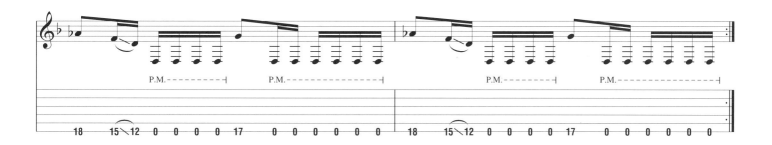

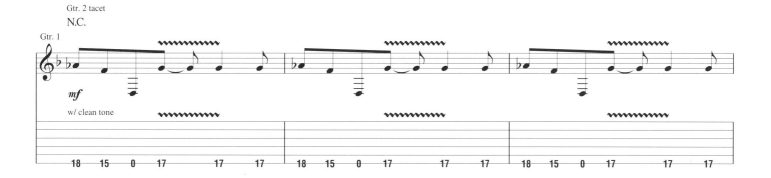

3rd time, half-time feel

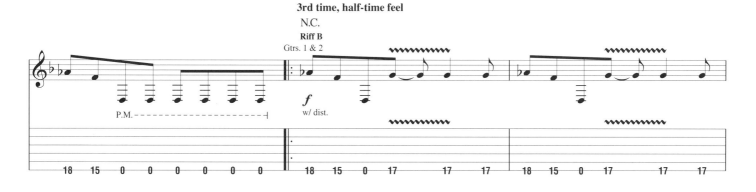

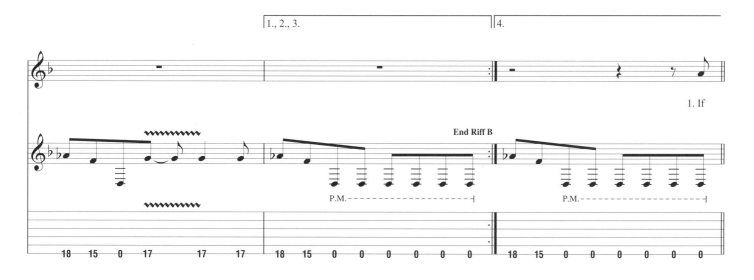

Verse

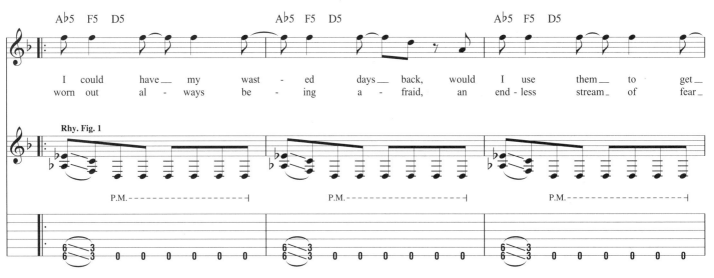

I could have ___ my wast - ed days ___ back, would I use them ___ to get ___
worn out al - ways be - ing a - fraid, an end - less stream ___ of fear ___

Gtr. 1: w/ Rhy. Fig. 1 (1st 3 meas.)
Gtr. 2: w/ Rhy. Fig. 1

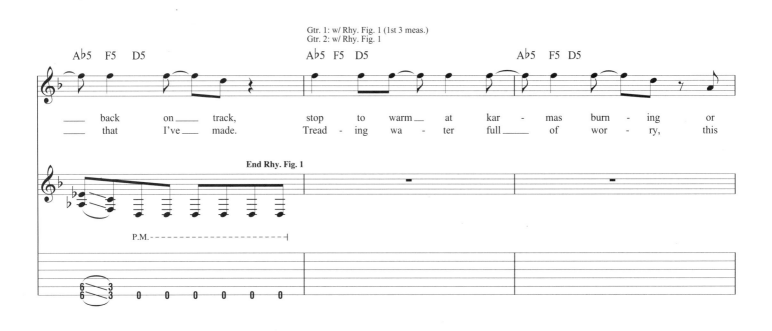

___ back on ___ track, stop to warm ___ at kar - mas burn - ing or
___ that I've ___ made. Tread - ing wa - ter full ___ of wor - ry, or this

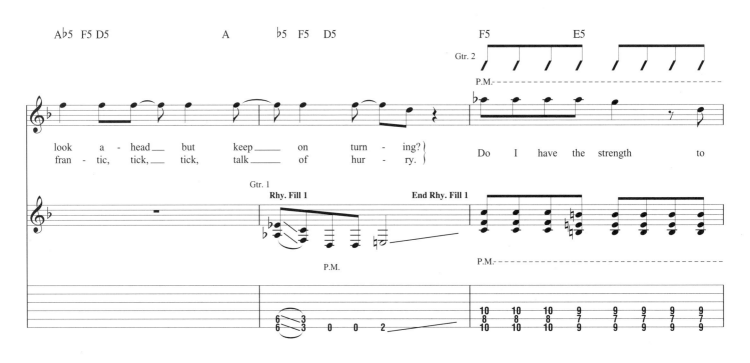

look a - head ___ but keep ___ on turn - ing?
fran - tic, tick, ___ tick, talk ___ of hur - ry.

Do I have the strength to

52

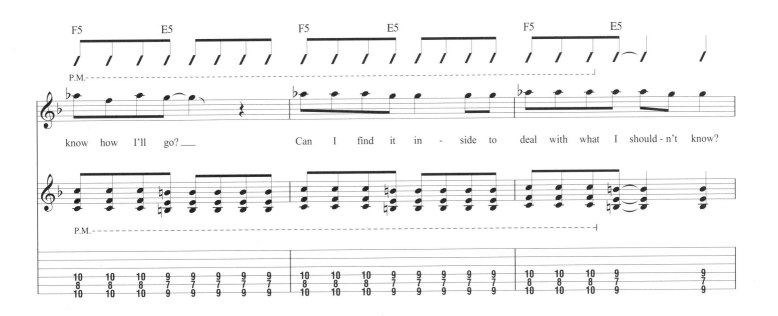

know how I'll go?___ Can I find it in - side to deal with what I should - n't know?

End half-time feel

{ Could I have___ my wast - ed days___ back? Would I use them___ to get___ back on___ track? }
{ Worn out al - ways be - ing a - fraid, an end - less stream___ of fear___ that I've___ made. }

You live it or lie___ it! You

live it or lie___ it! (You live it or lie___ it! You live it or lie___ it! My

life - style   de -ter -mines my death - style.   My life - style   de - ter - mines my death - style.

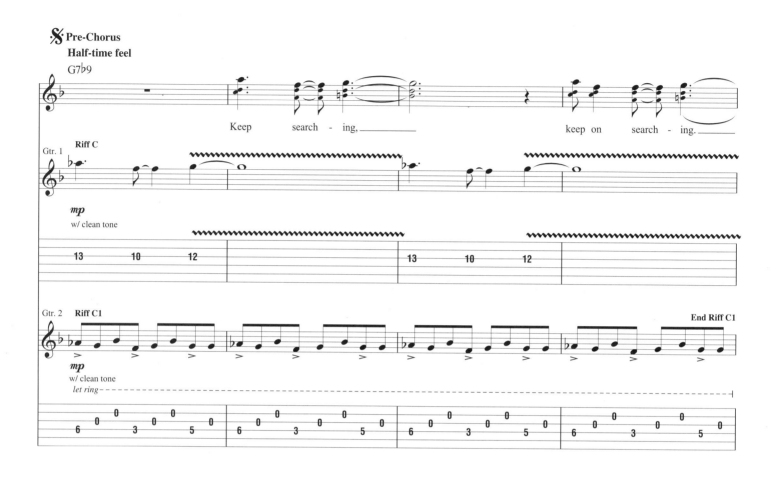

Pre-Chorus
Half-time feel

Keep   search - ing,_____   keep on   search - ing._____

Gtr. 1   **Riff C**

mp
w/ clean tone

Gtr. 2   **Riff C1**   **End Riff C1**

mp
w/ clean tone
let ring

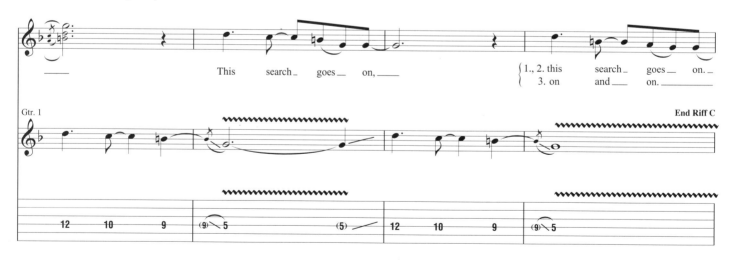

Gtr. 2: w/ Riff C1 (3 times)

This   search_   goes_   on,_____   1., 2. this   search_   goes_   on._
                                        3. on   and ___   on._____

Gtr. 1   **End Riff C**

Gtr. 1: w/ Riff C

Keep   search - ing,_____   keep on   search - ing._____

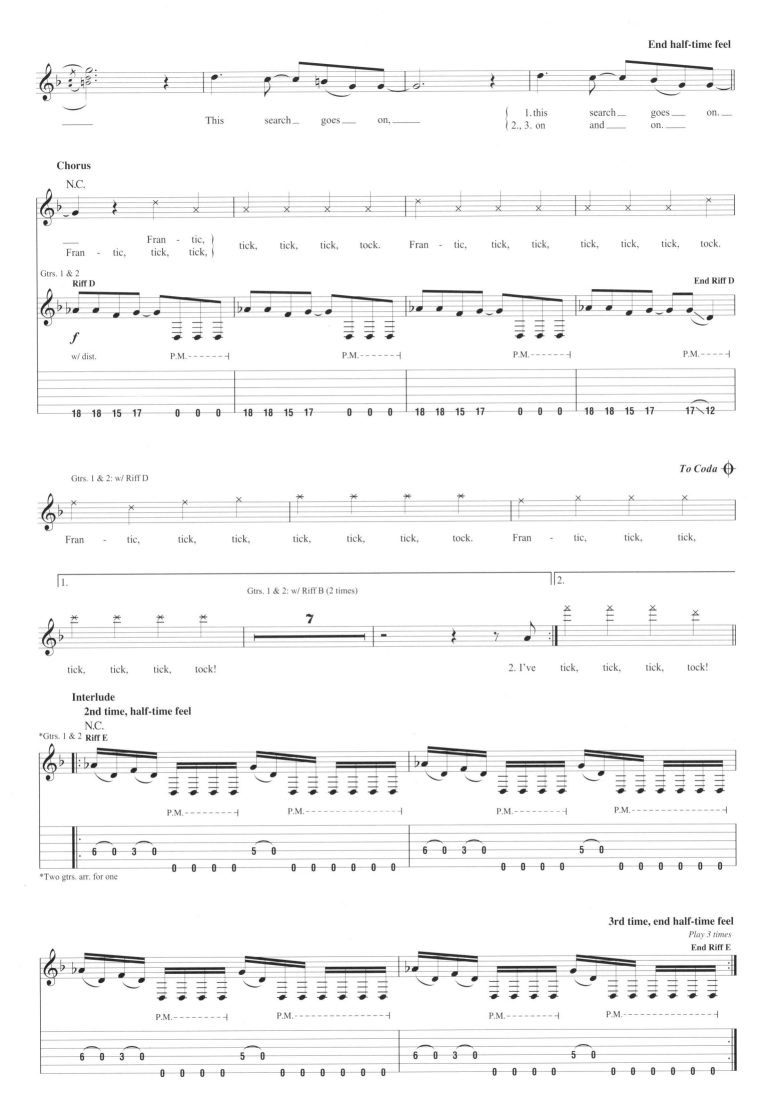

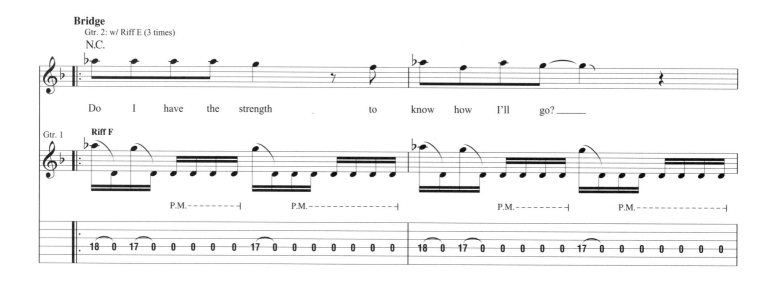

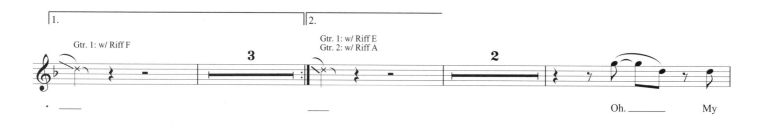

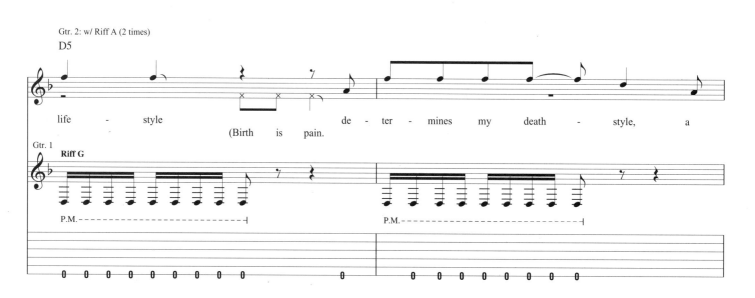

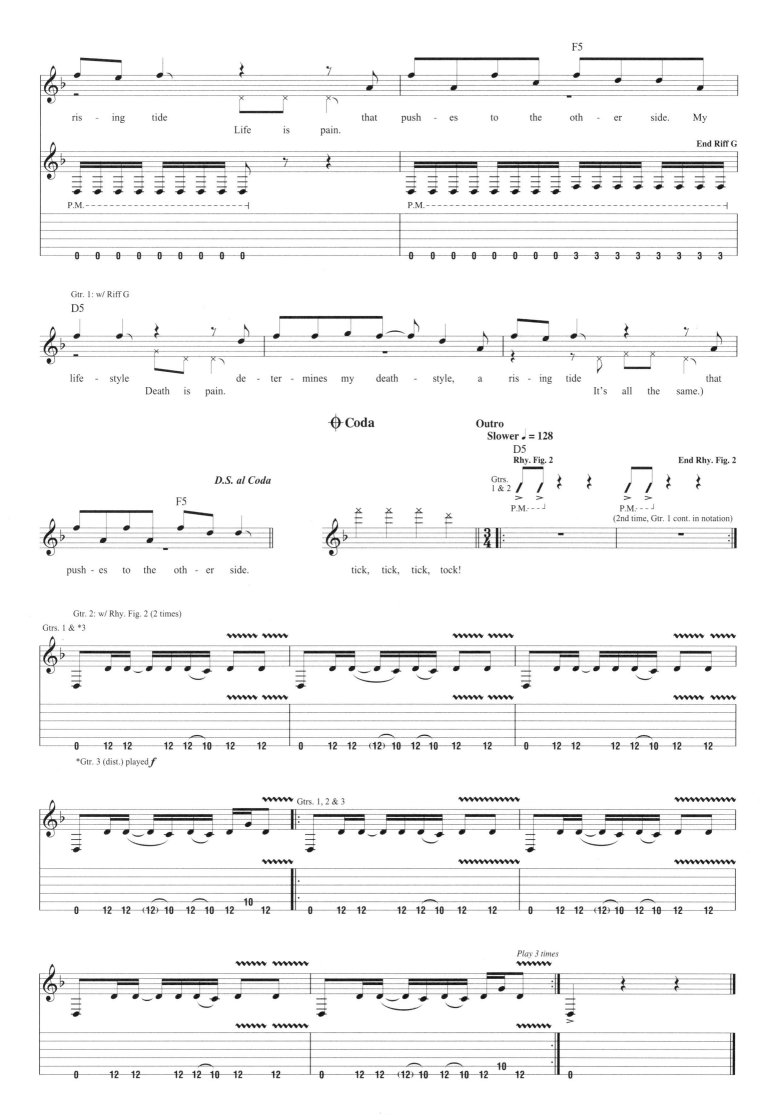

JUST BECAUSE

WORDS & MUSIC BY PERRY FARRELL, DAVE NAVARRO, CHRIS CHANEY, STEPHEN PERKINS & BOB EZRIN

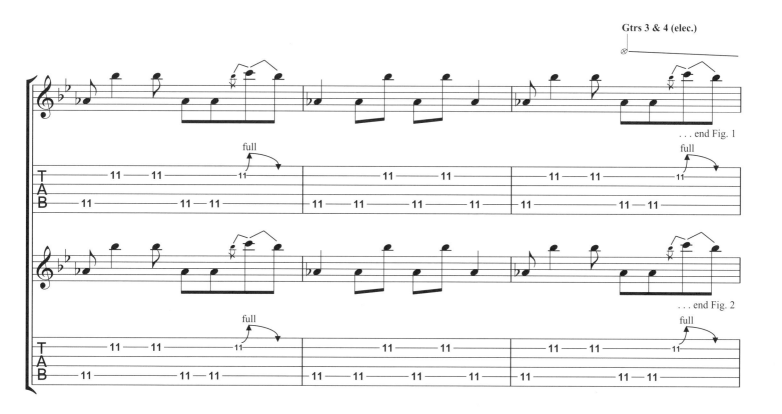

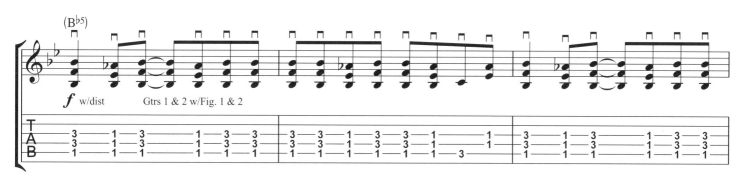

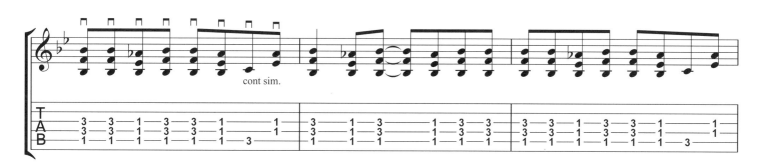

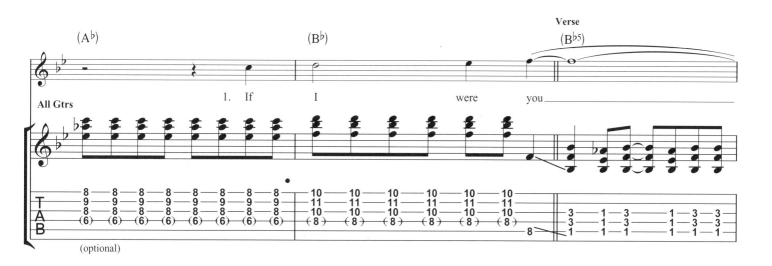

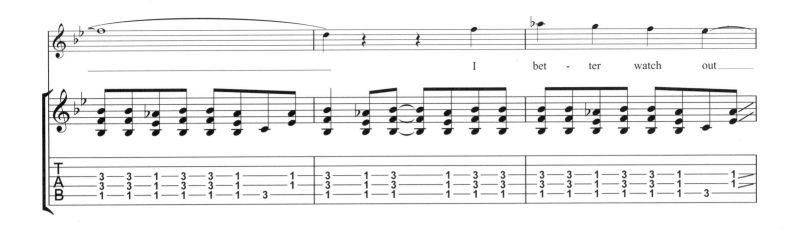

I bet - ter watch out

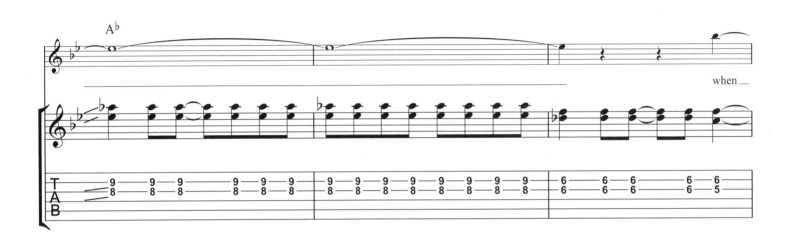

when

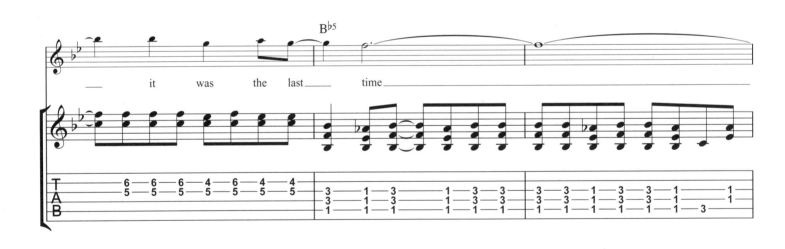

it was the last time

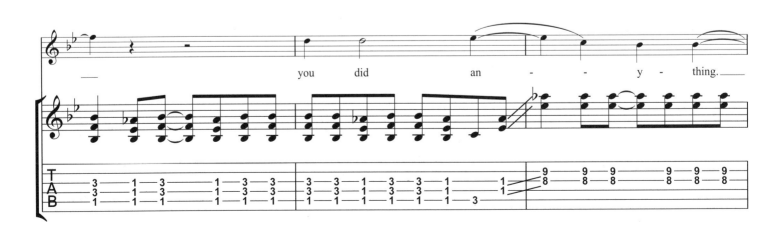

you did an - y - thing.

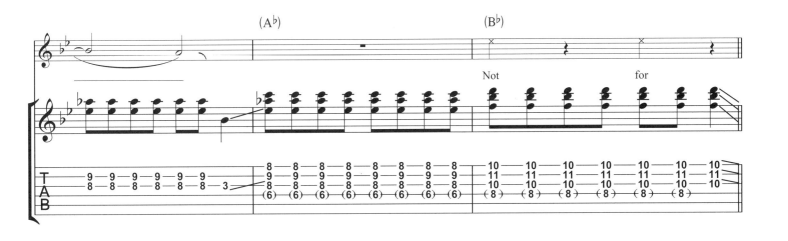

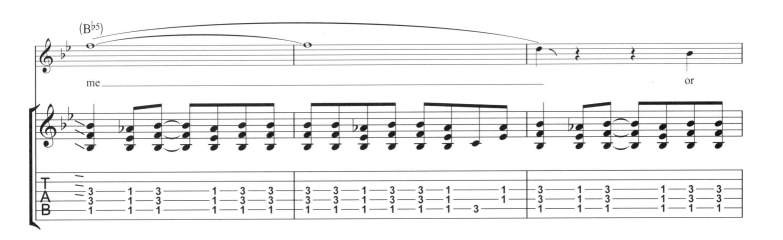

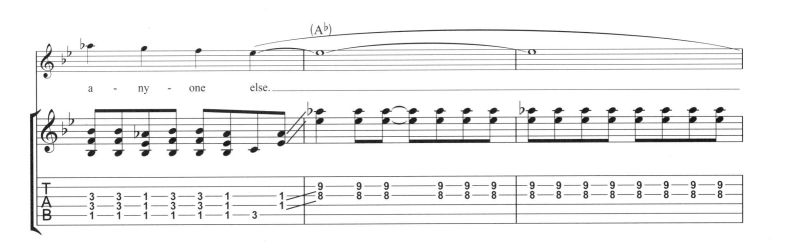

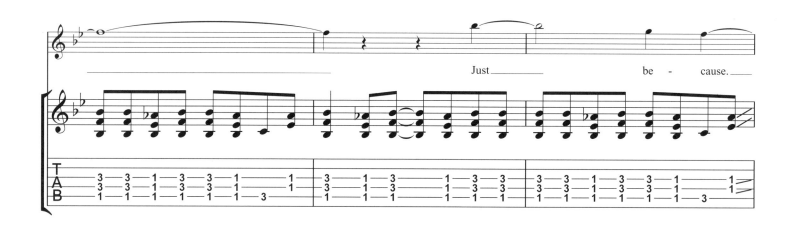

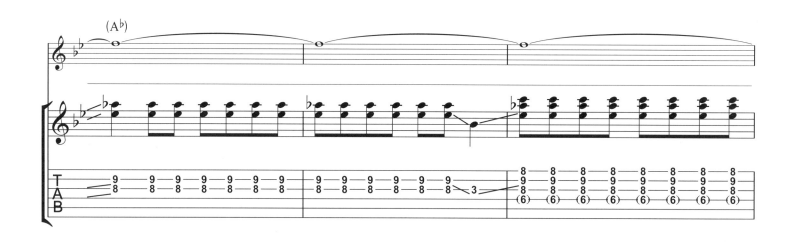

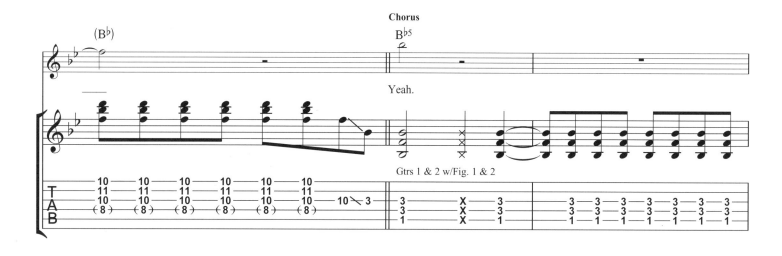

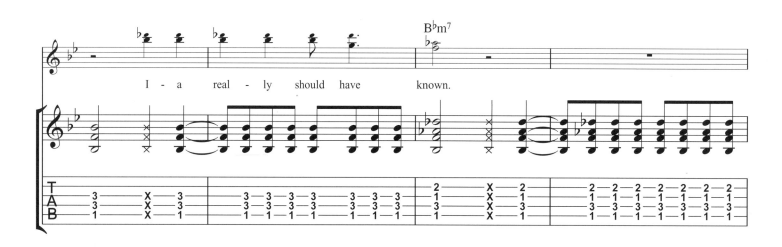

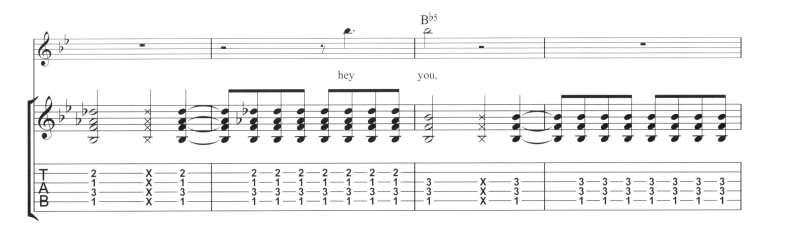

hey you,

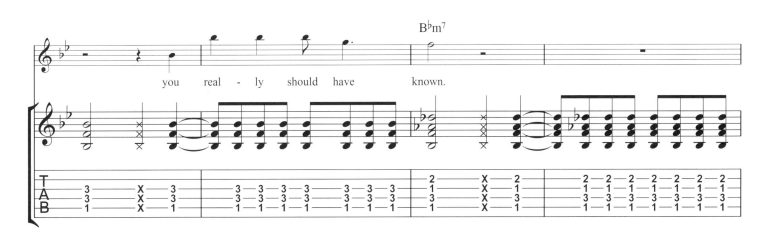

you real - ly should have known.

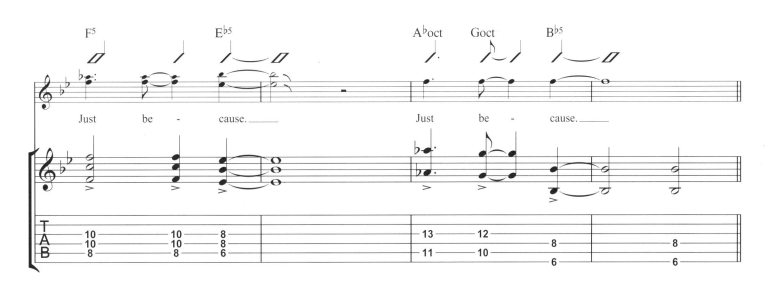

Just be - cause. _____   Just be - cause. _____

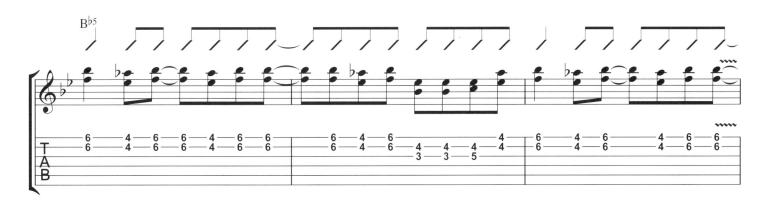

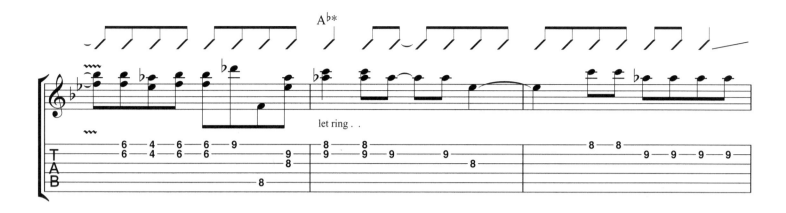

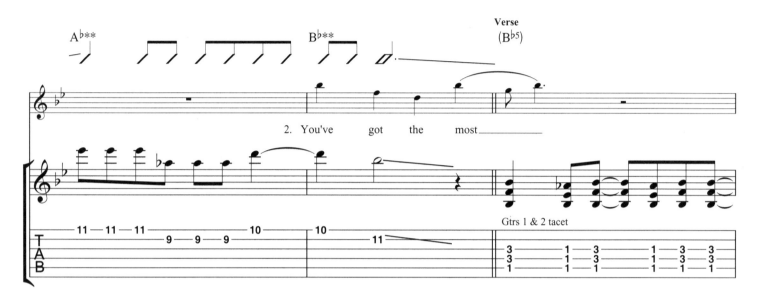

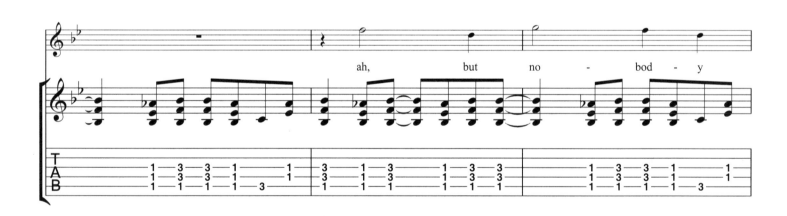

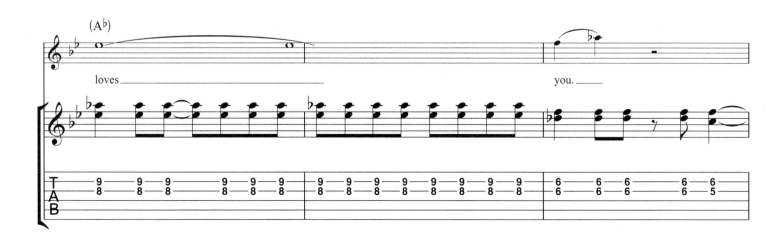

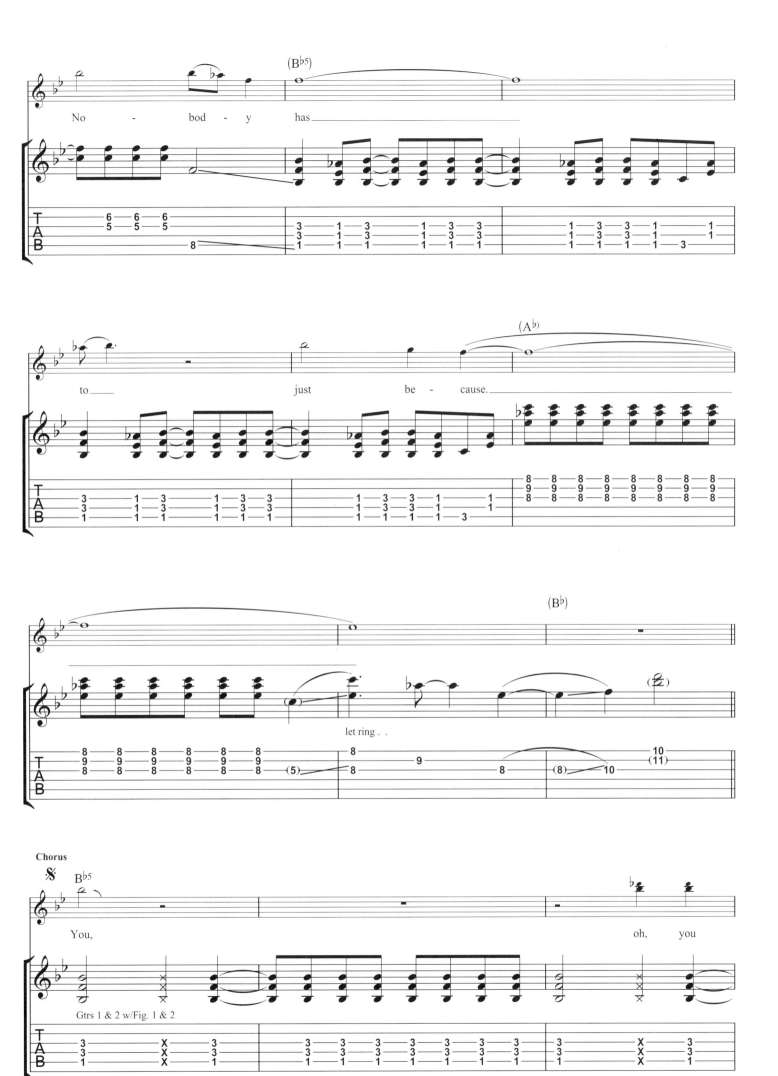

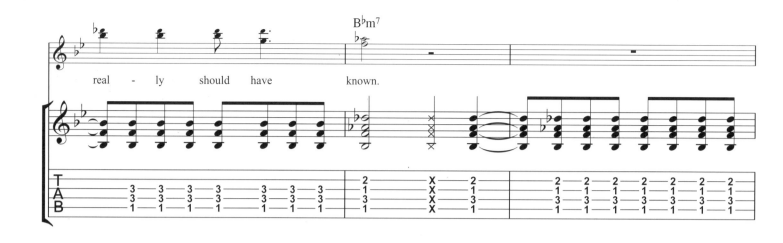

real - ly should have known.

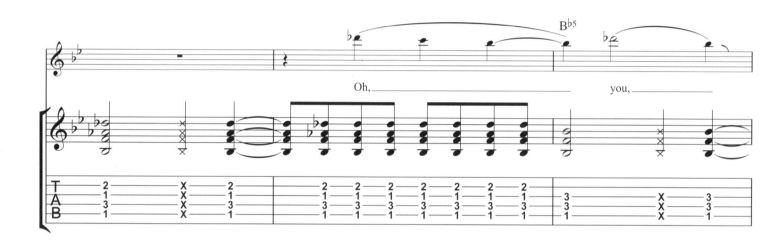

Oh, you,

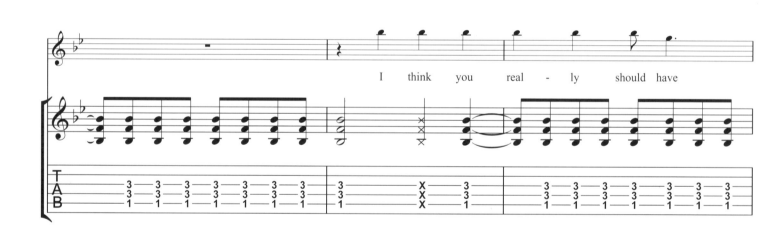

I think you real - ly should have

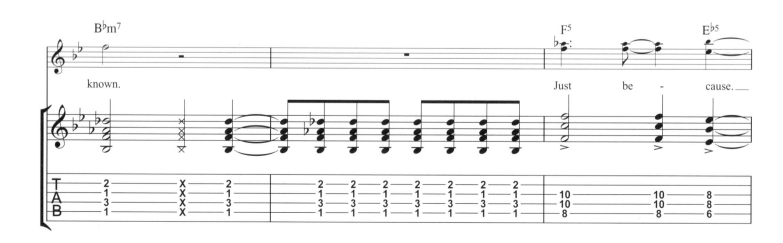

known. Just be - cause.

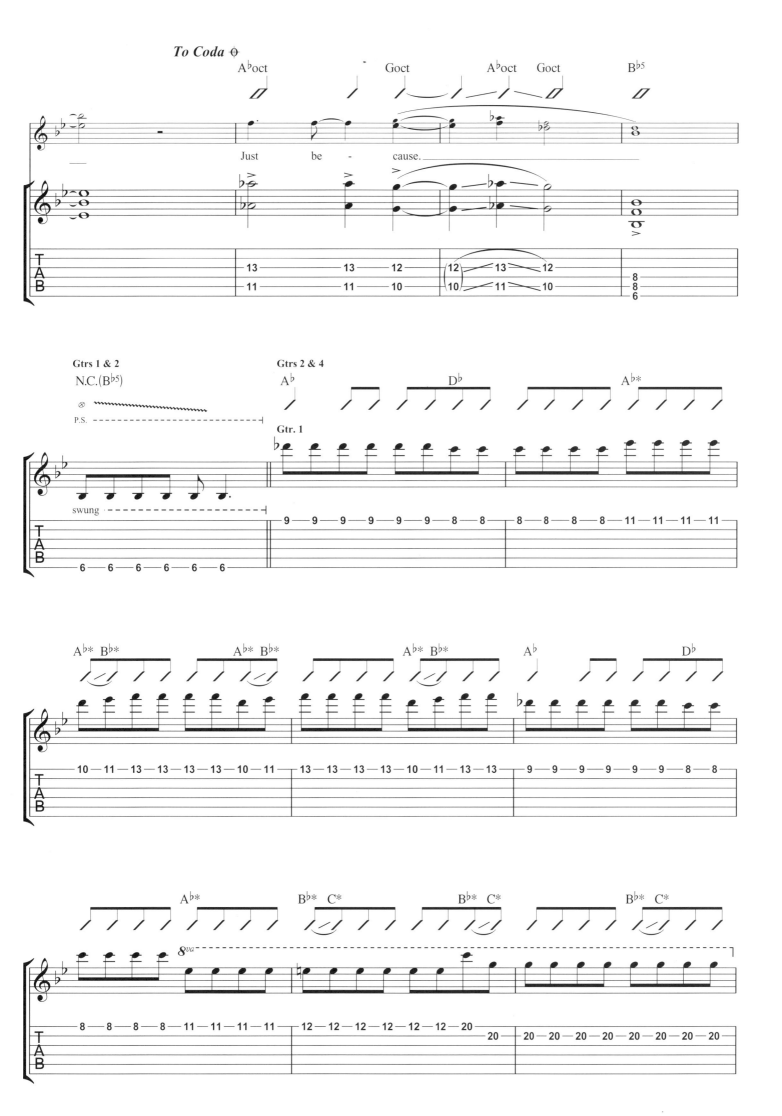

3. When we first met.

Gtr. 3

Gtrs 1 & 2 tacet

and we passed a - round.

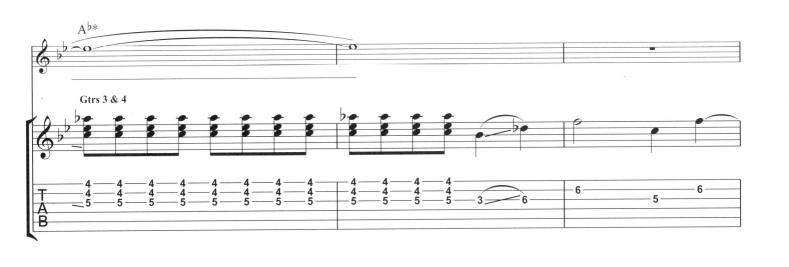

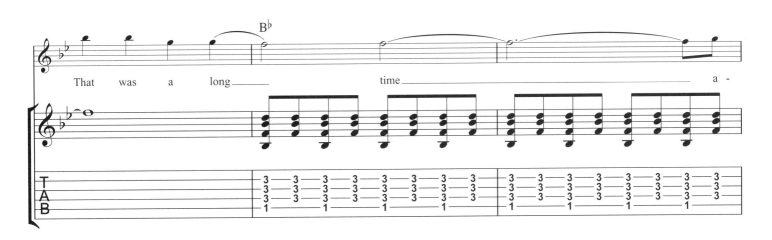

That was a long_____ time_____ a-

-go and you're still in bed._____

D.S. al Coda

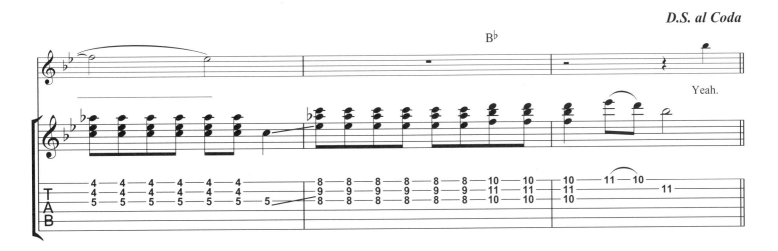

Yeah.

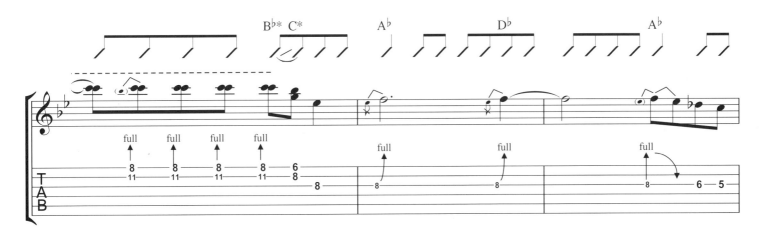

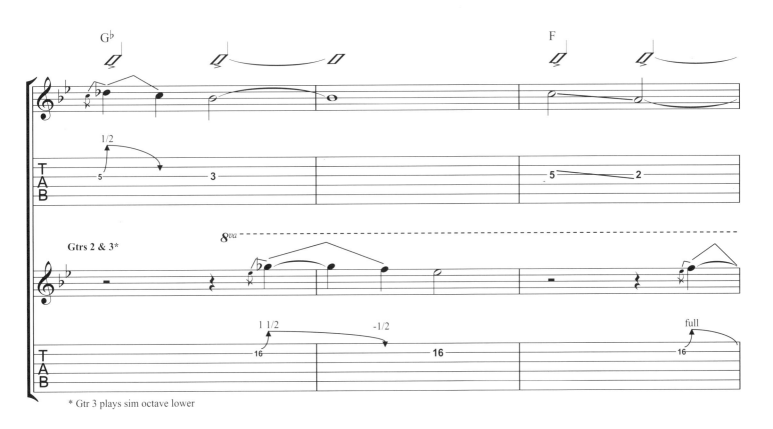

* Gtr 3 plays sim octave lower

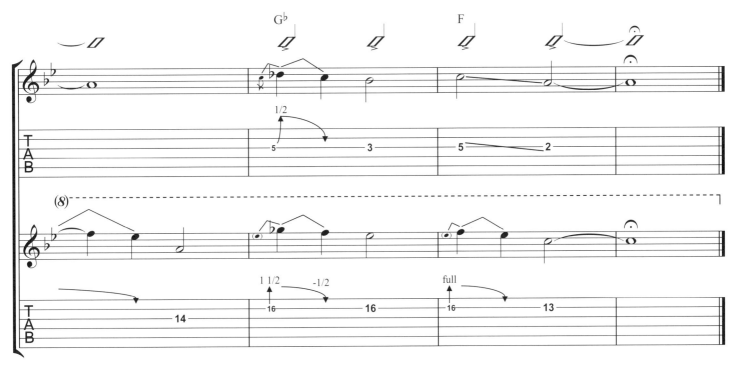

LAST TRAIN HOME

WORDS & MUSIC BY IAN WATKINS, LEE GAZE, MIKE LEWIS, STUART RICHARDSON, MIKE CHIPLIN & JAMIE OLIVER

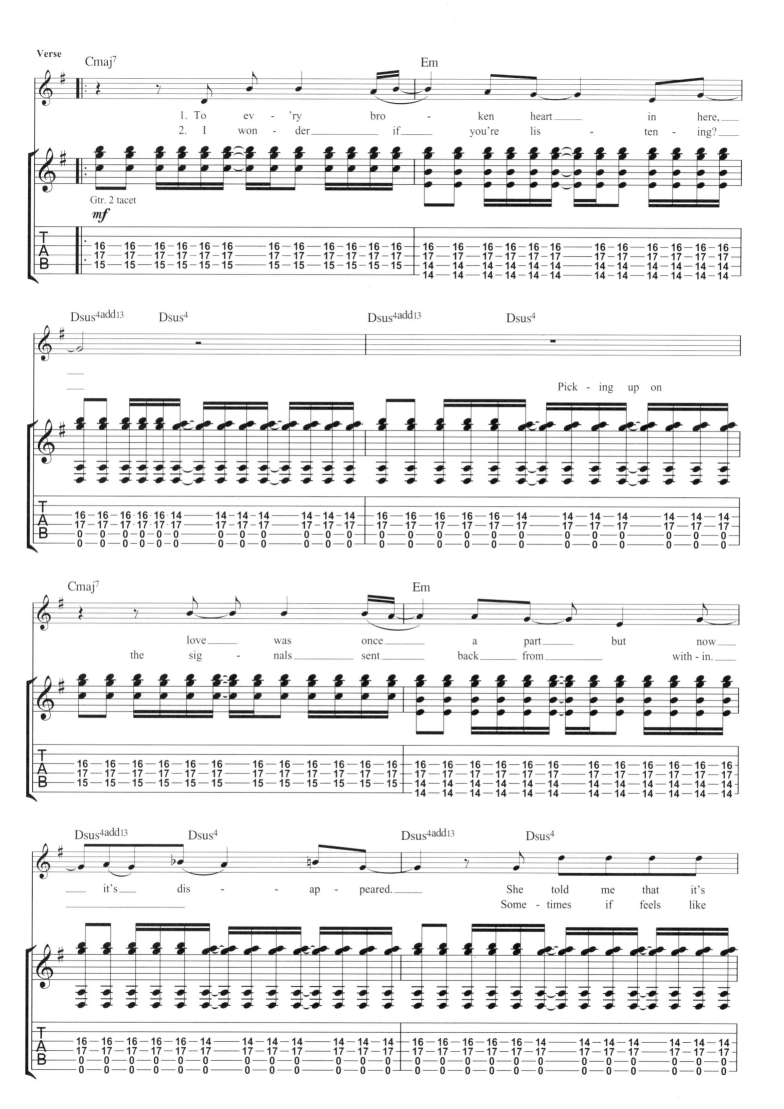

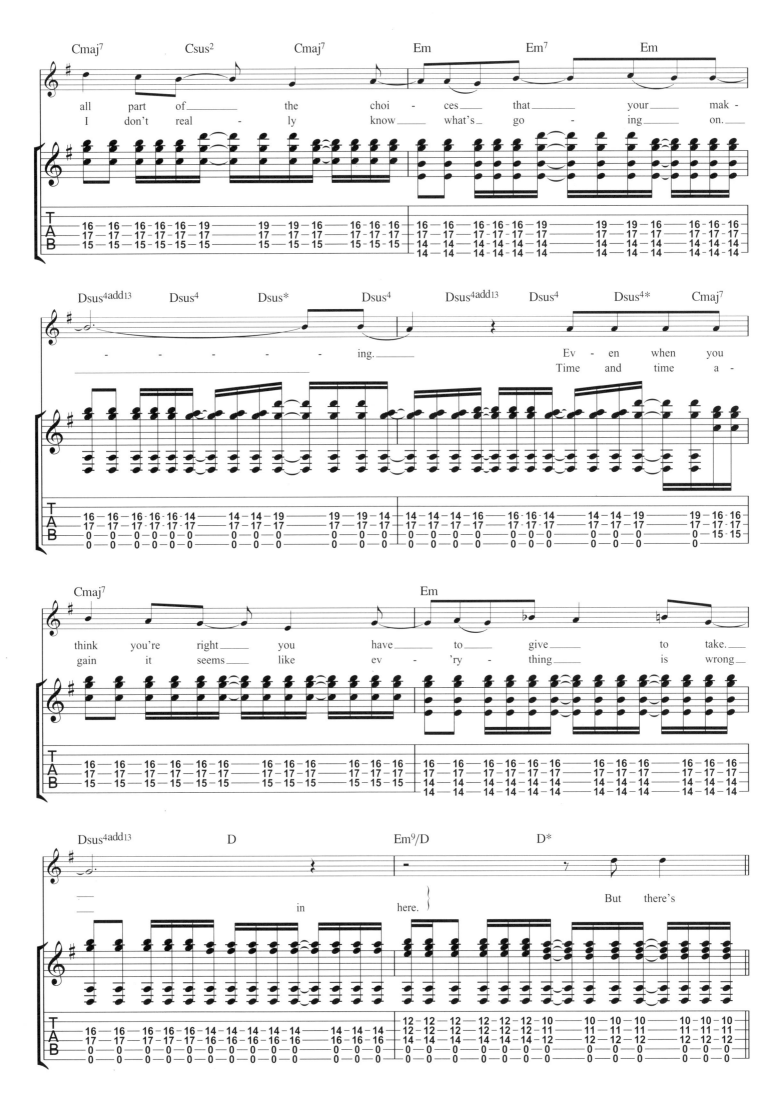

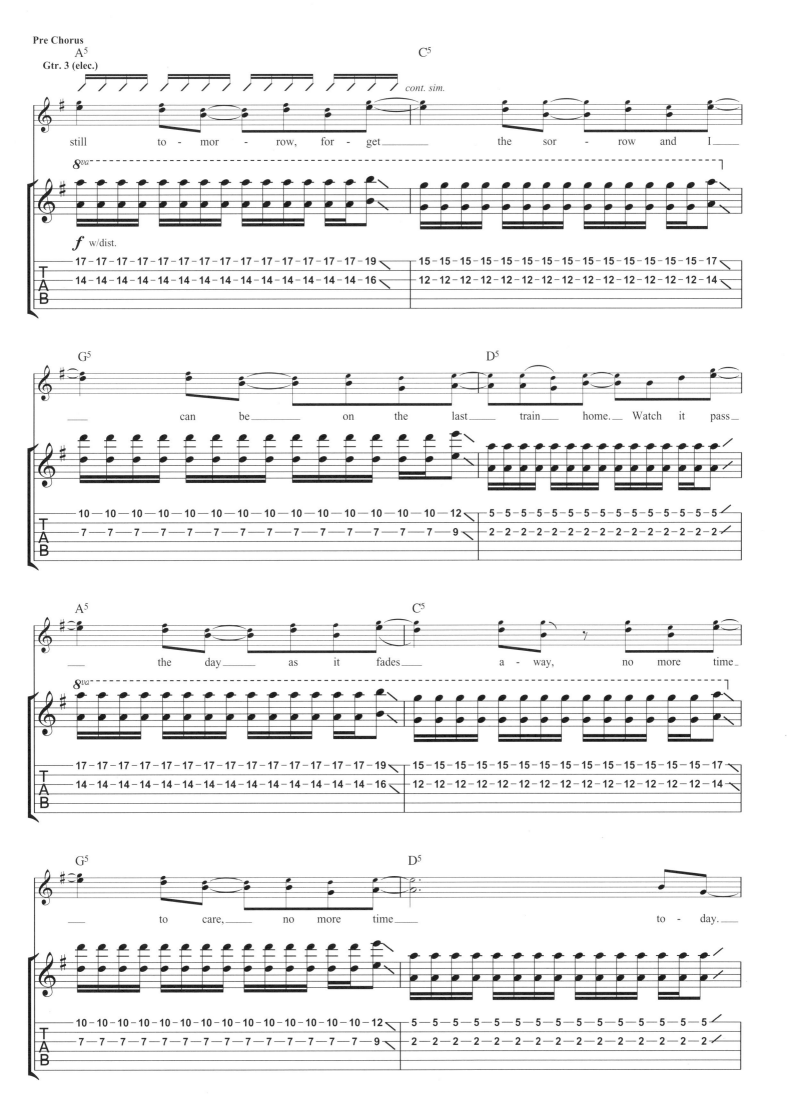

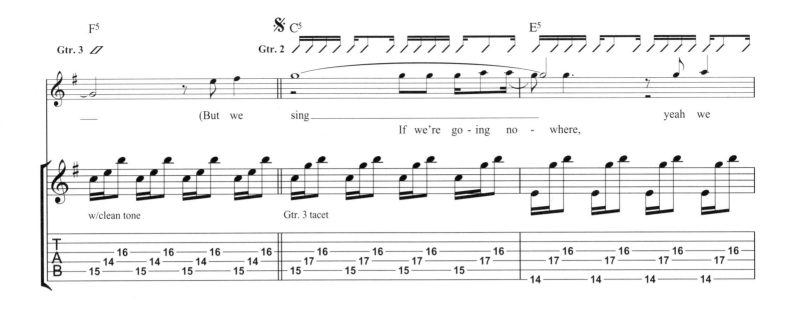

(But we sing _____ yeah we
If we're go - ing no - where,

w/clean tone   Gtr. 3 tacet

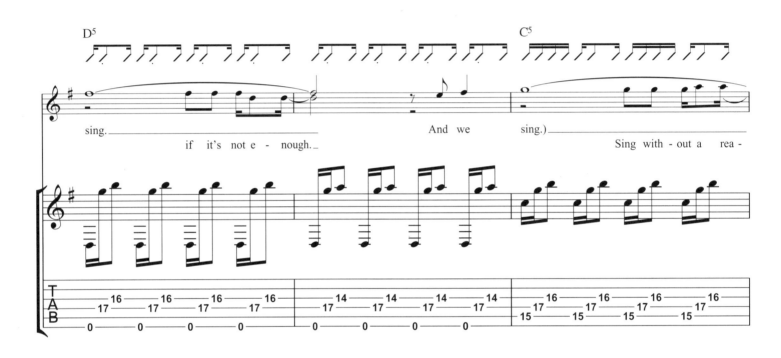

sing. _____
if it's not e - nough. _
And we   sing.)
Sing with - out a rea -

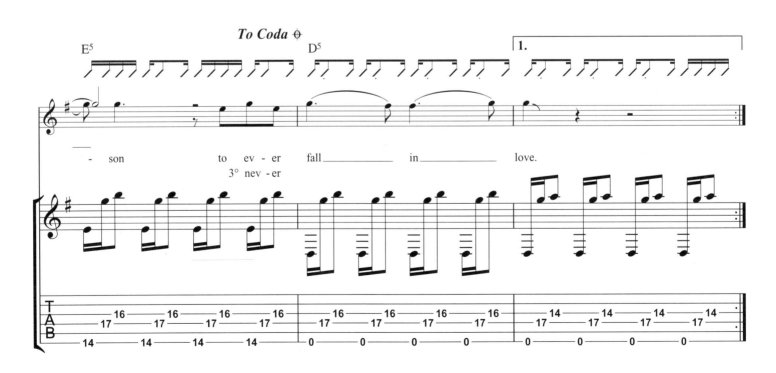

To Coda ⊕

- son   to ev - er fall _____ in _____ love.
3° nev - er

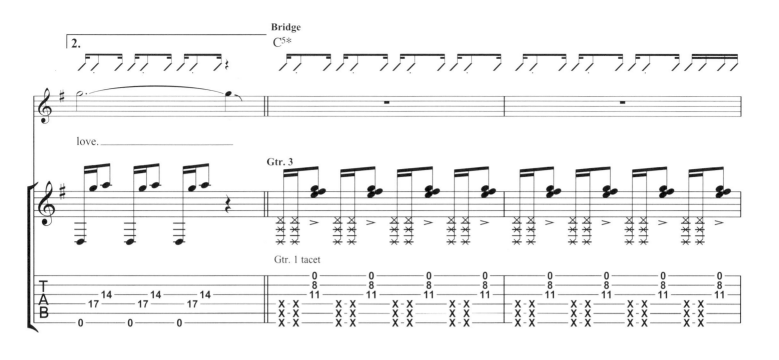

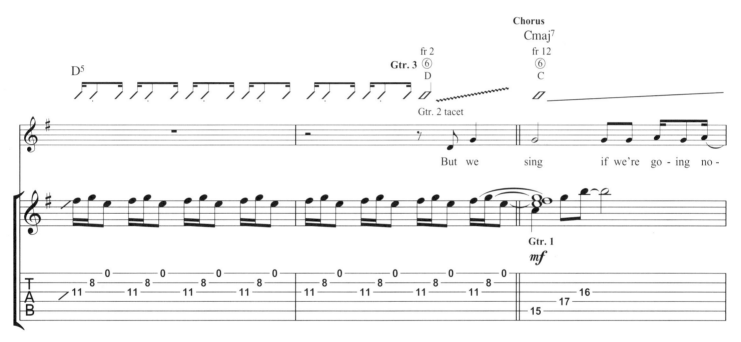

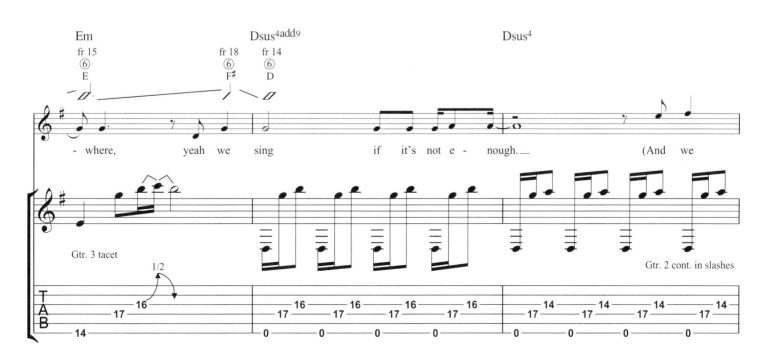

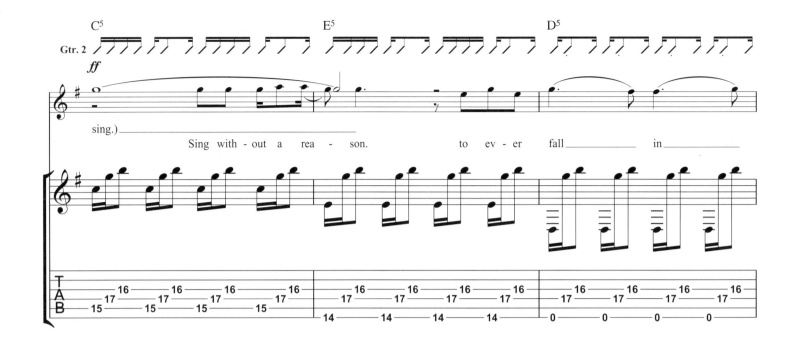

Sing with - out a rea - son. to ev - er fall ____ in ____

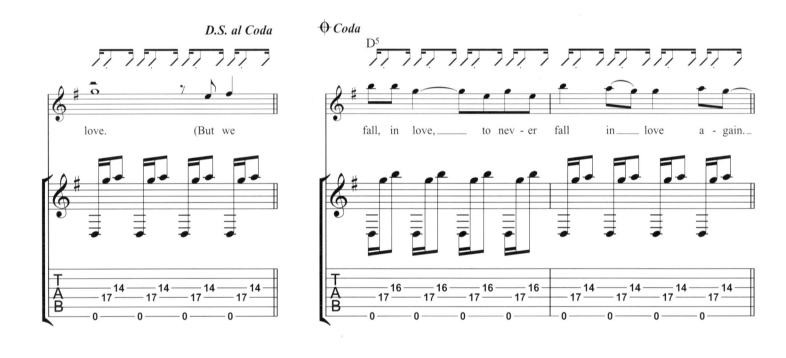

love. (But we

fall, in love, ____ to nev - er fall in ____ love a - gain.

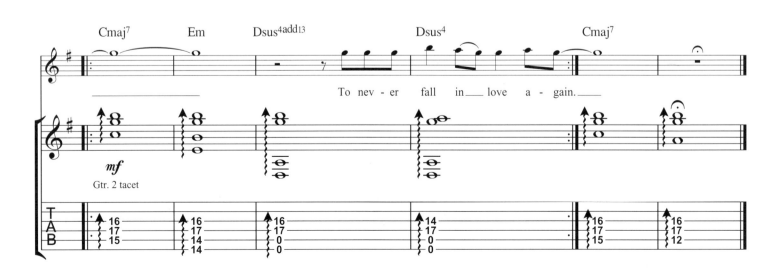

To nev - er fall in ____ love a - gain. ____

LITTLE KNOW IT ALL

WORDS & MUSIC BY IGGY POP, DERYCK WHIBLEY & GREIG NORI

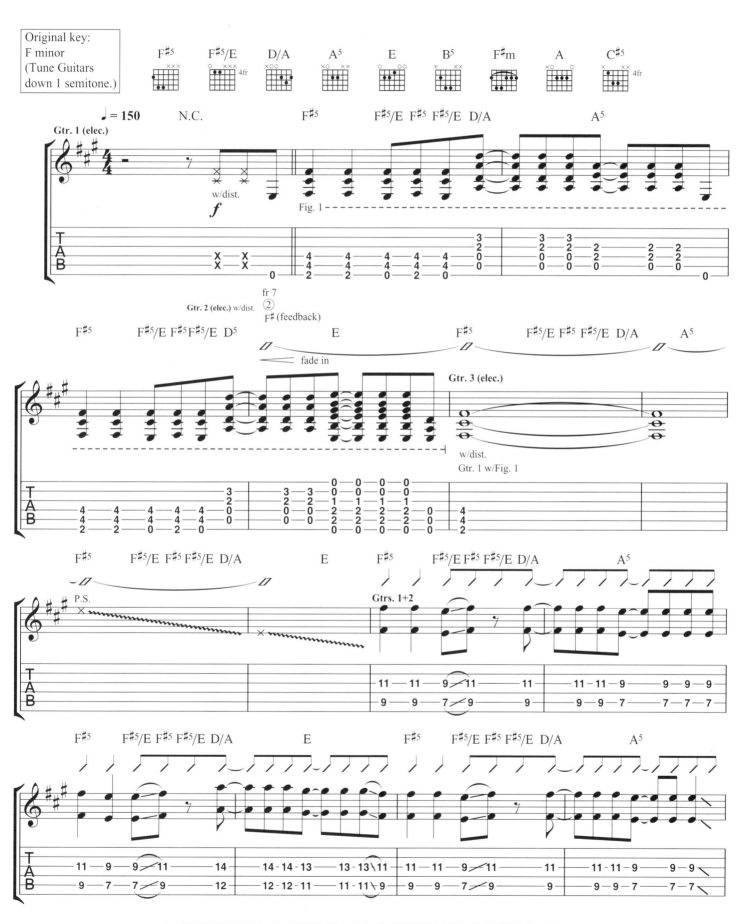

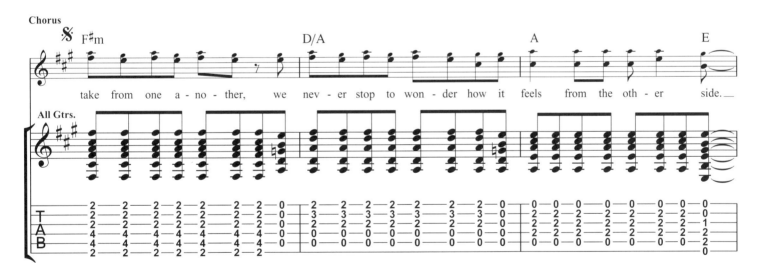

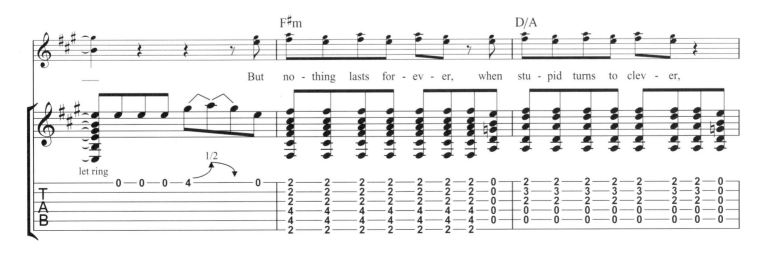

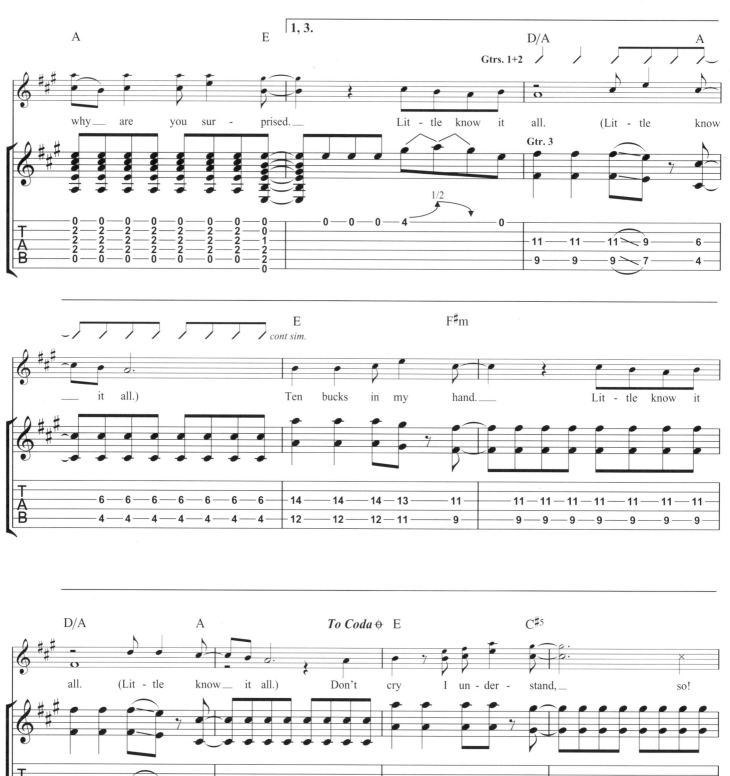

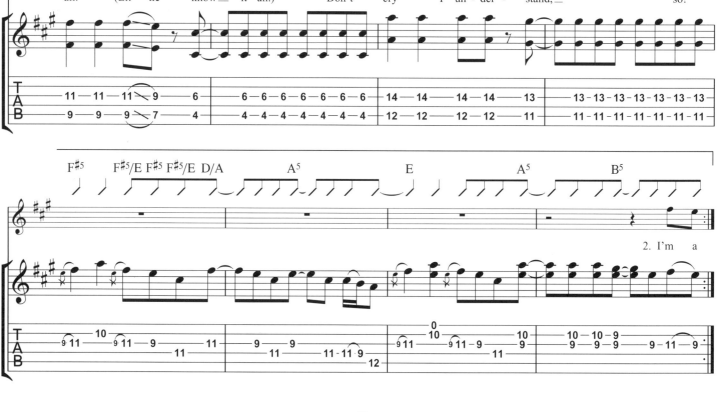

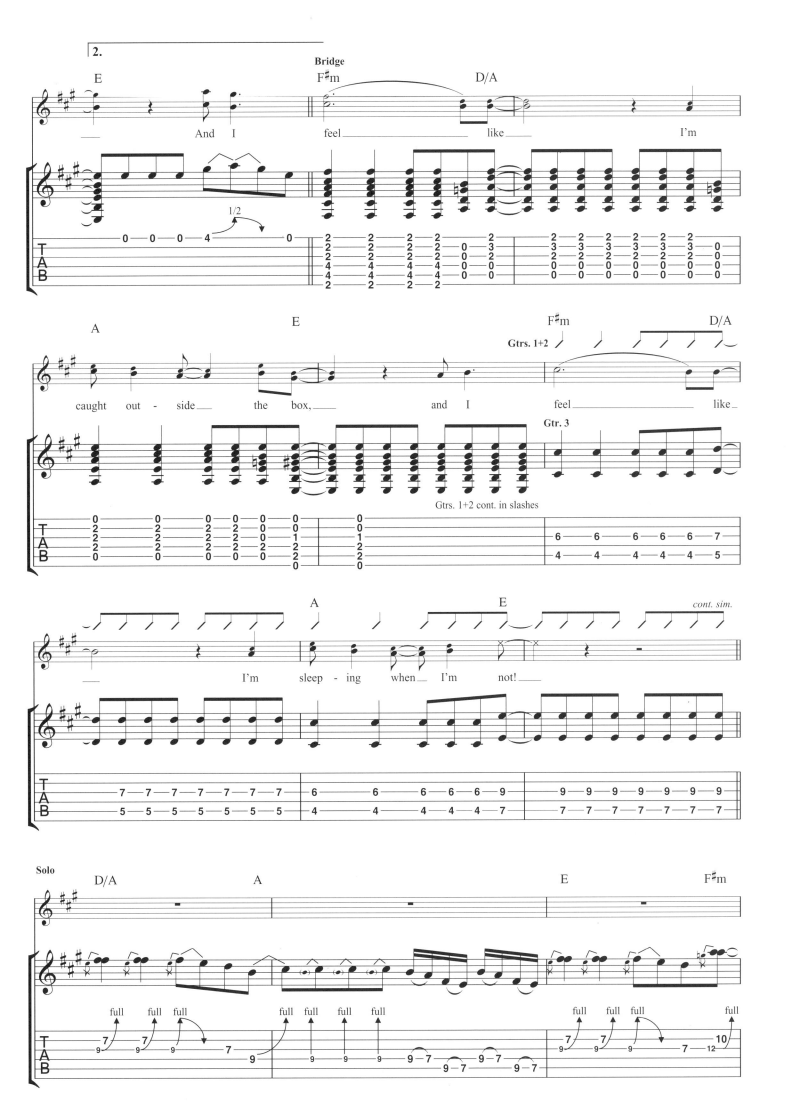

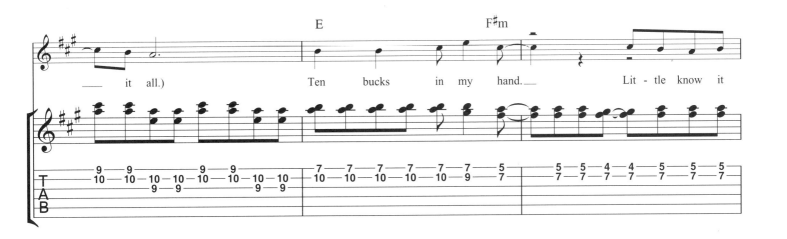

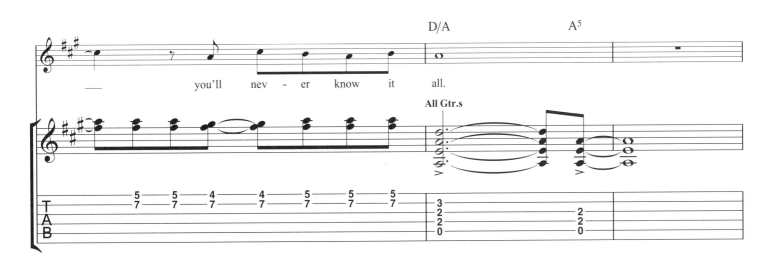

THE LOST ART OF KEEPING A SECRET

WORDS & MUSIC BY JOSH HOMME & NICK OLIVERI

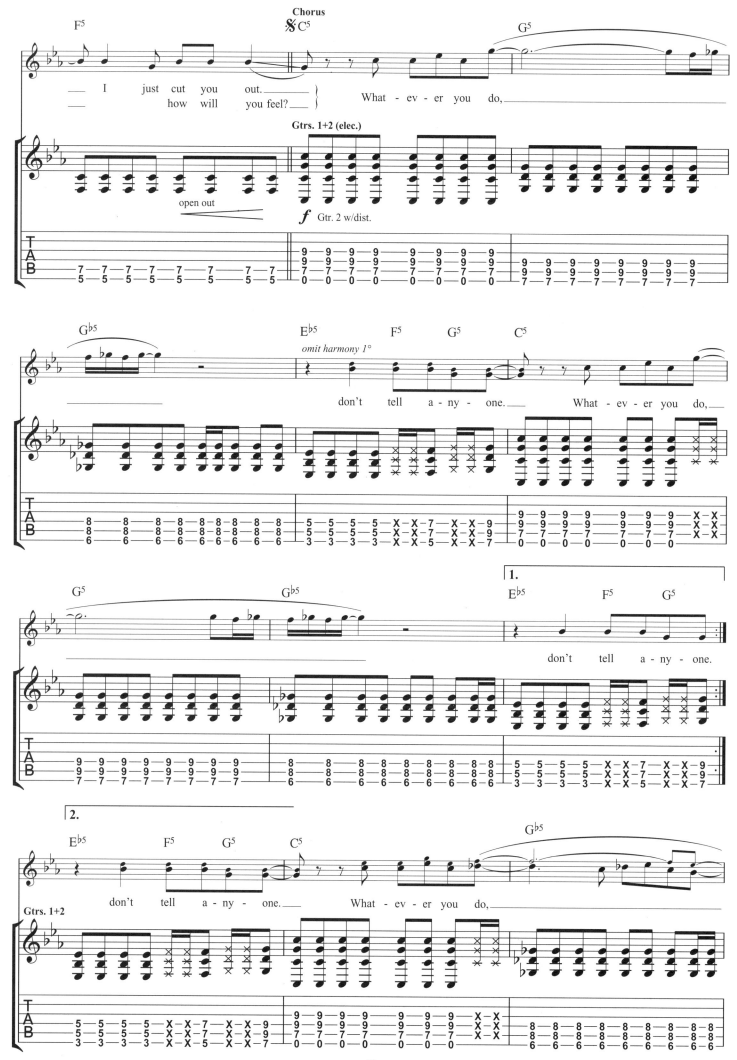

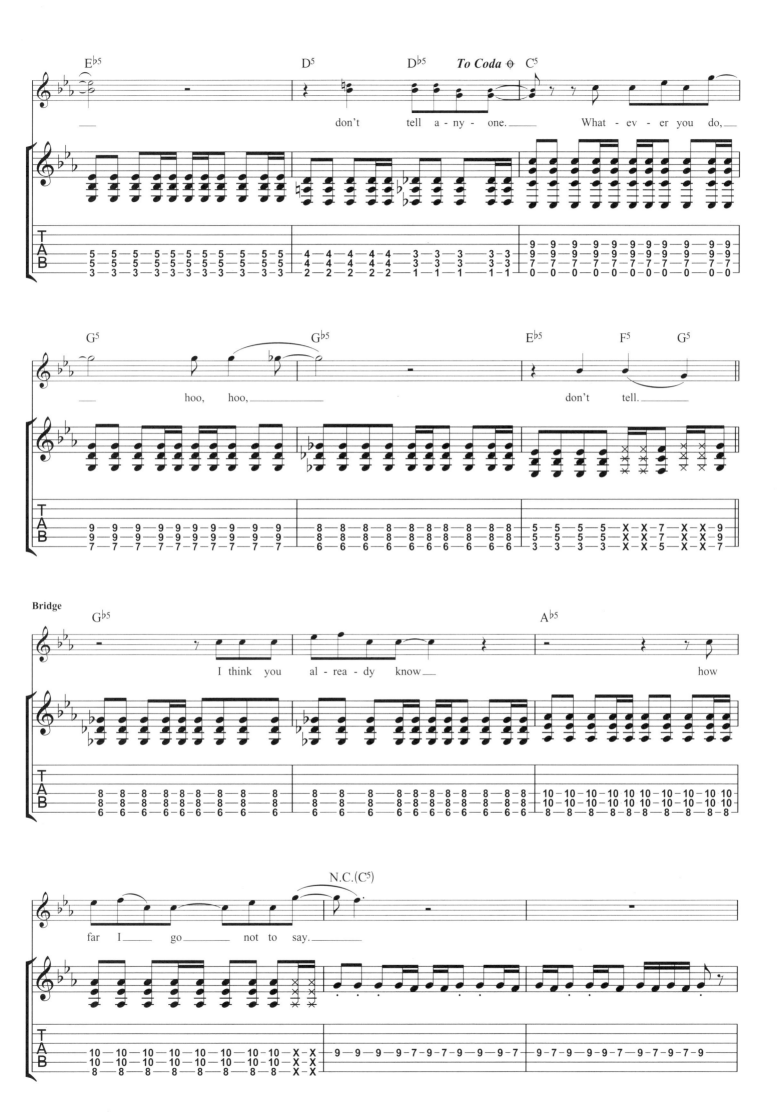

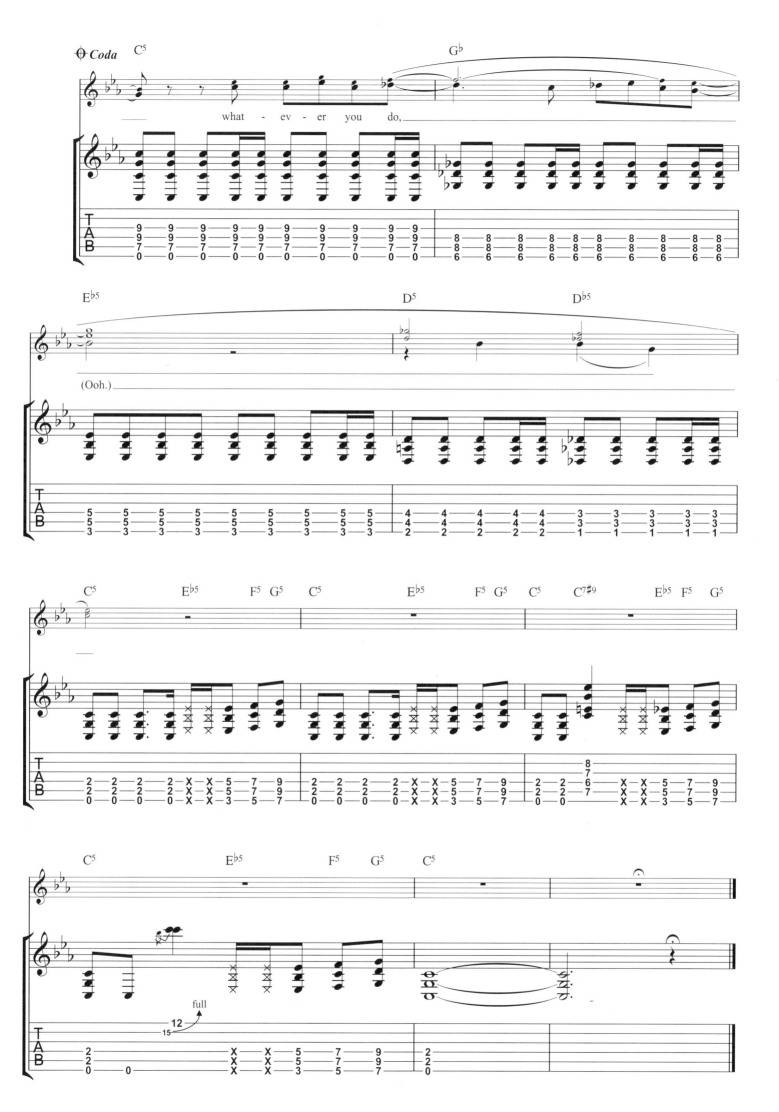

Mobscene

Words by Marilyn Manson
Music by John 5 & Marilyn Manson

bleed, that's why she'll nev - er stay._____ A -
soul with whis - pers in your ear._____ O.

2° Gtr. 3 plays fig. 2

Gtr. 3

Fig. 2 -

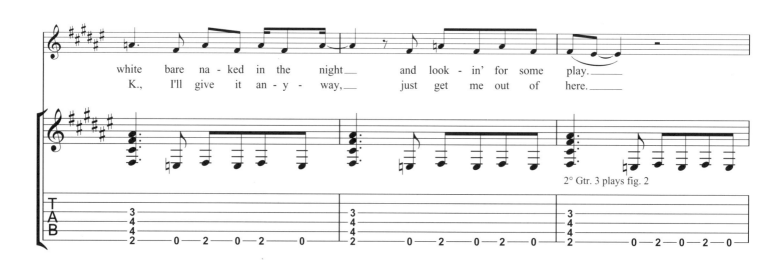

white bare na - ked in the night_____ and look - in' for some play._____
K., I'll give it an - y - way,_____ just get me out of here._____

2° Gtr. 3 plays fig. 2

A - just a - no - ther girl_____ that wants to run the world_____ at a - ny - time_____ or_____
You'll plead, you'll get down on your knees_____ for just a - no - ther_____

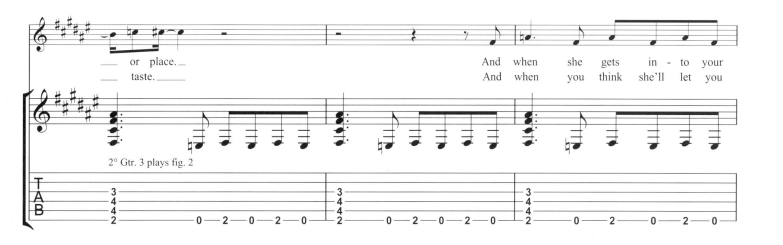

___ or place.___
___ taste._____

And when she gets in - to your
And when you think she'll let you

2° Gtr. 3 plays fig. 2

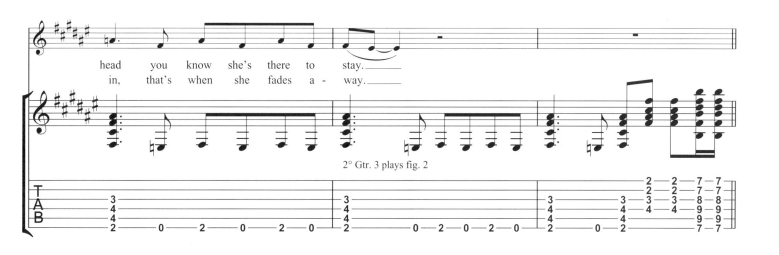

head you know she's there to stay._____
in, that's when she fades a - way._____

2° Gtr. 3 plays fig. 2

Chorus

B   A   F♯   F♯/E   F♯   F♯/E   F♯   F♯/E

Gtr. 2

You want it,   she's got it;___   Mol - ly's cham - bers gon - na

Gtrs. 1+2

Gtr. 3

2° only

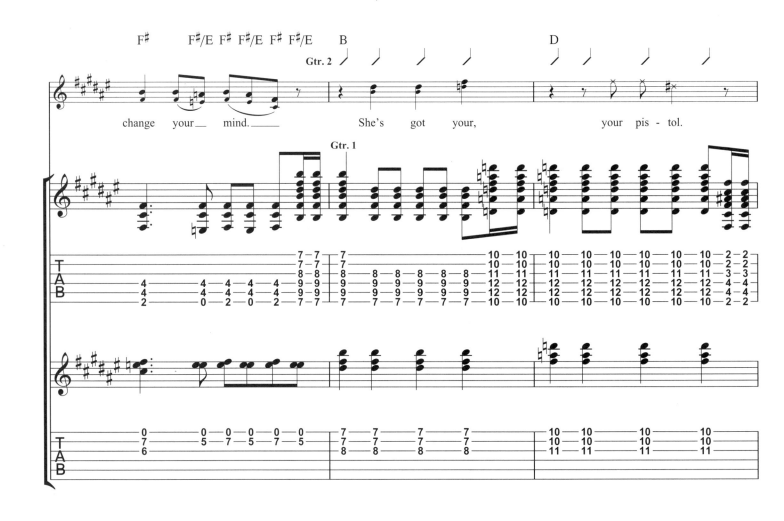

change your mind. She's got your, your pis-tol.

Mol-ly's cham-bers gon-na change your mind,

PLUG IN BABY

WORDS & MUSIC BY MATTHEW BELLAMY

Bass gtr. arr. for gtr.

Gtr. 1 tacet

Gtr. 1 cont. in cue notes

1. I've ex - posed your lies
2. Don't con - fuse

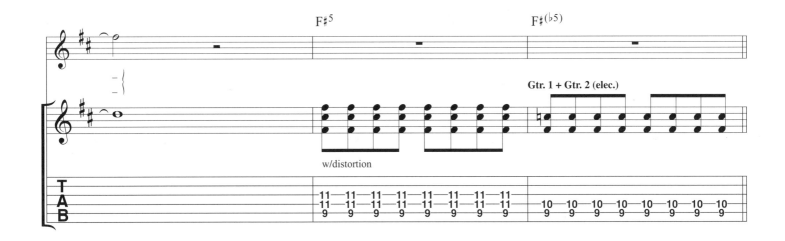

Chorus

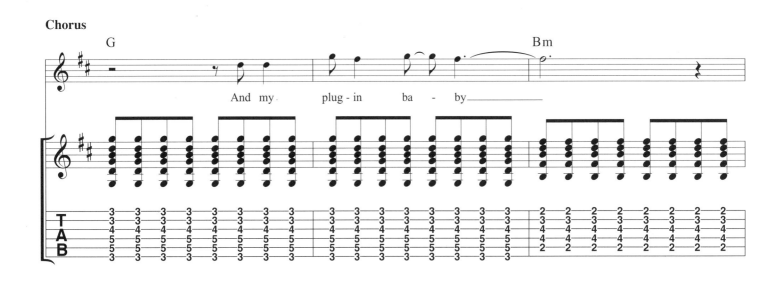

And my plug-in ba - by

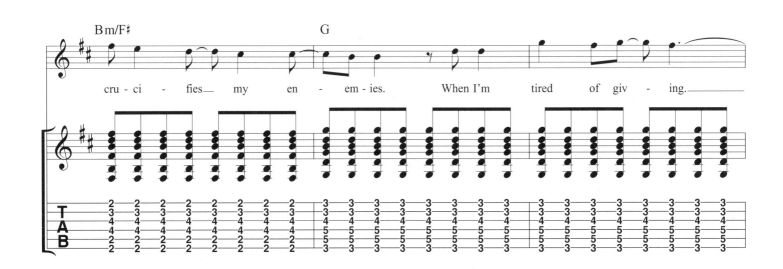

cru - ci - fies— my en - em - ies. When I'm tired of giv - ing.

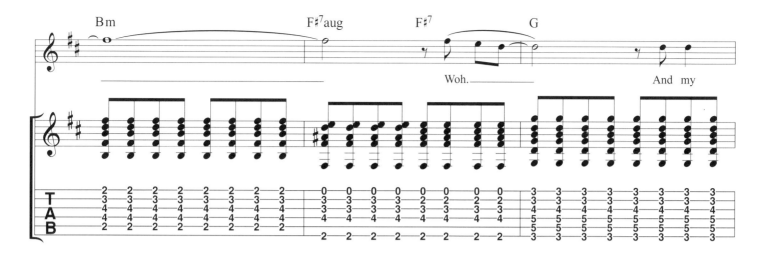

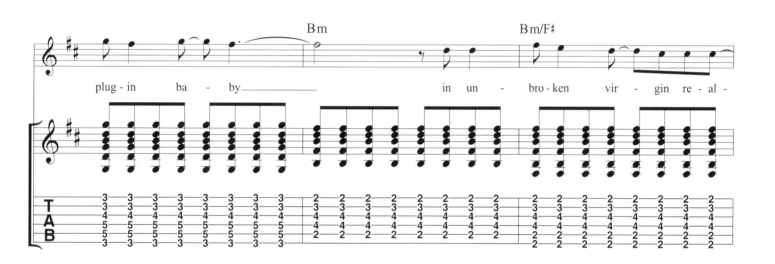

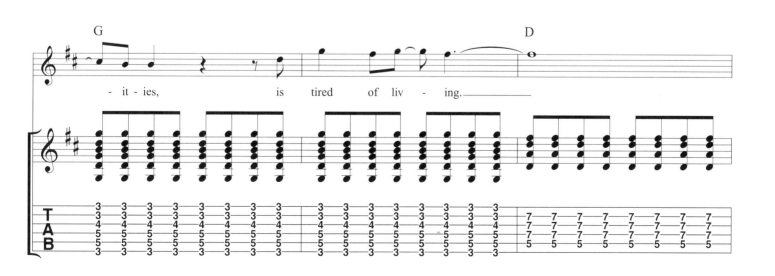

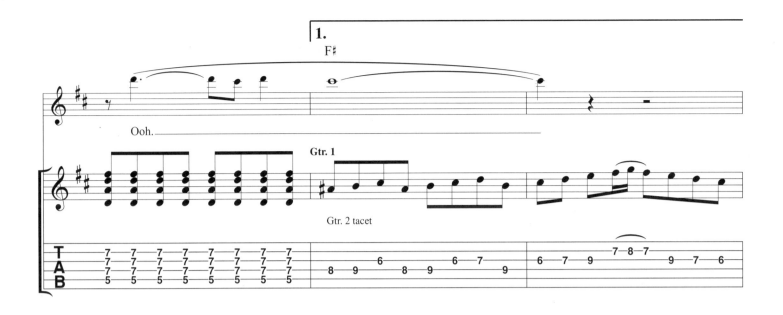

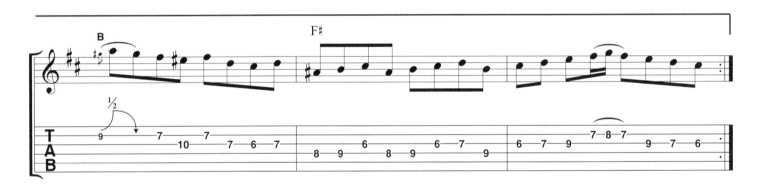

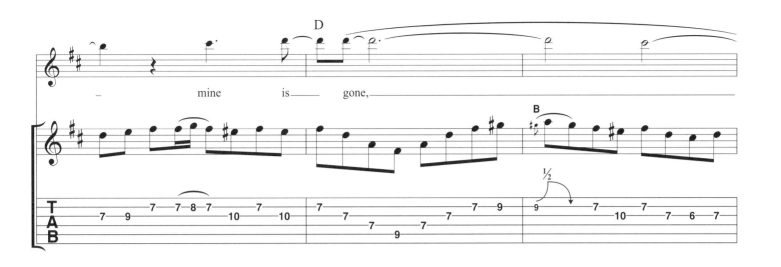

mine   is——   gone,——

—   and I've   been————   in——   trou -   ble.

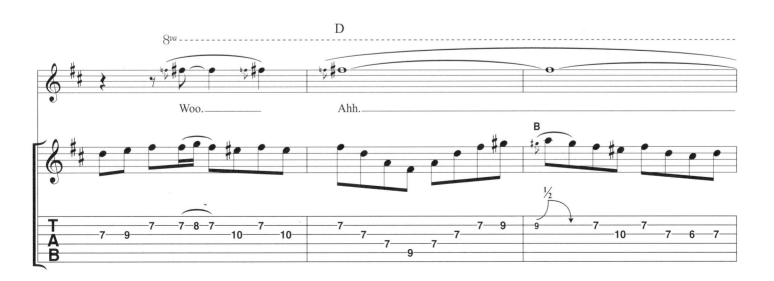

Woo.———   Ahh.———

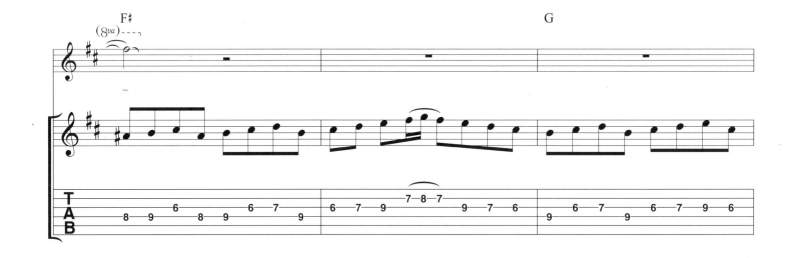

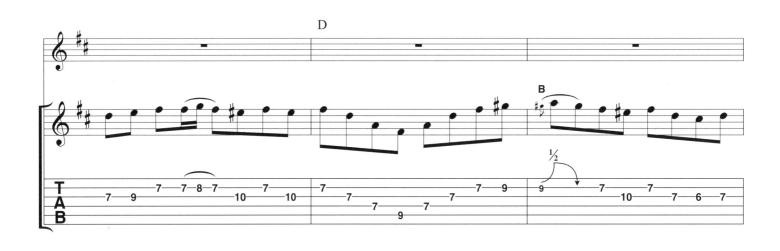

RAINMAKER

WORDS & MUSIC BY DAVID MURRAY, STEVE HARRIS & BRUCE

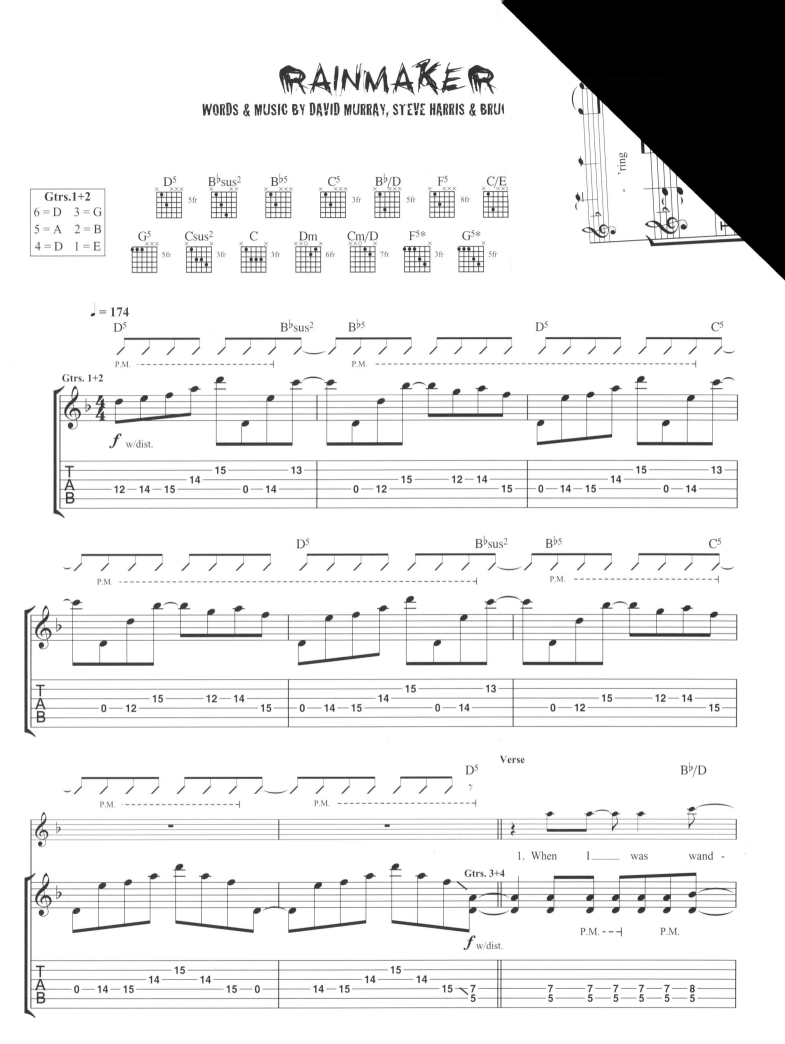

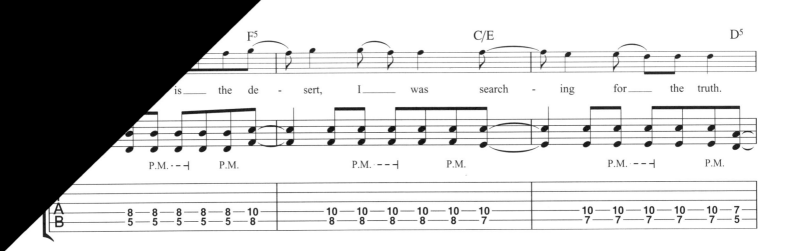

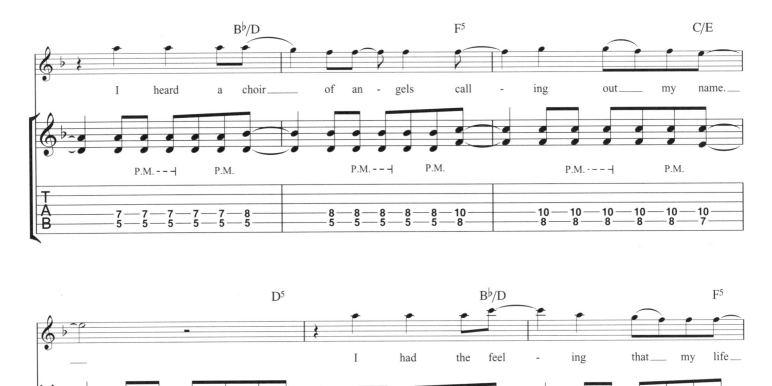

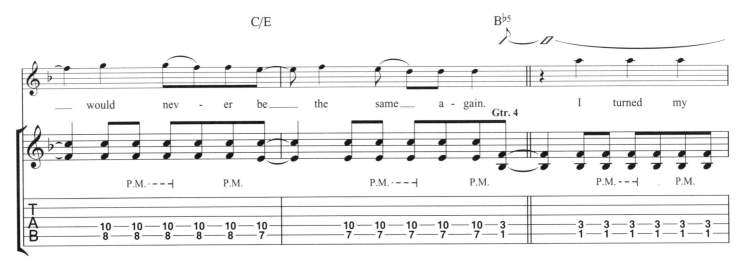

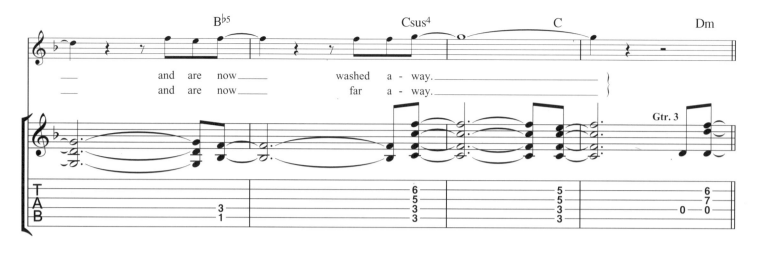

and are now____ washed a-way._____
and are now____ far a-way._____

Chorus

You tell____ me we____ can start____ the rain,____ you tell____ me that

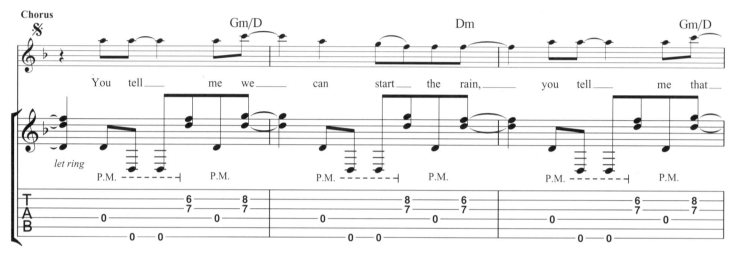

____ we all____ can change.____ You tell____ me we____ can find____ some-thing____

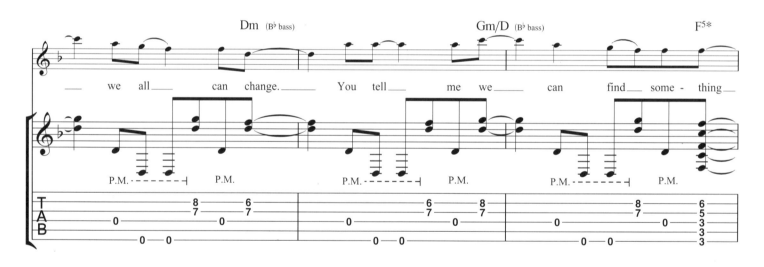

____ to wash____ the tears____ a-way.____ You tell____ me we____

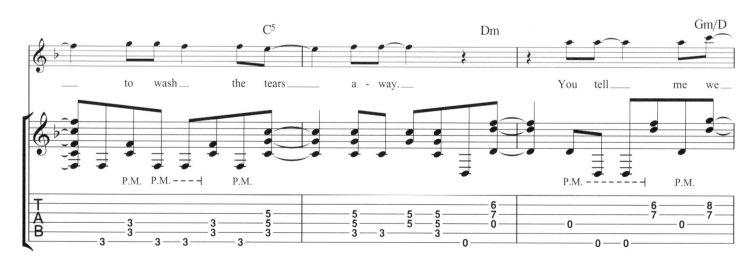

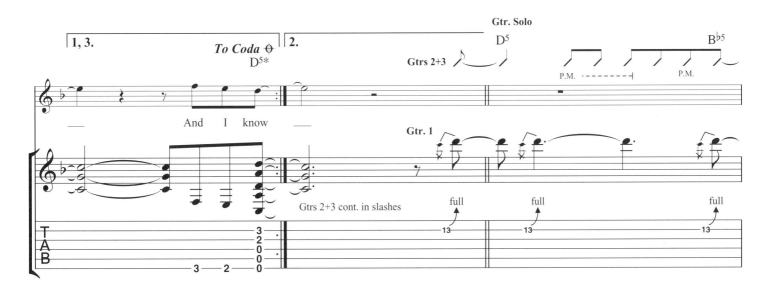

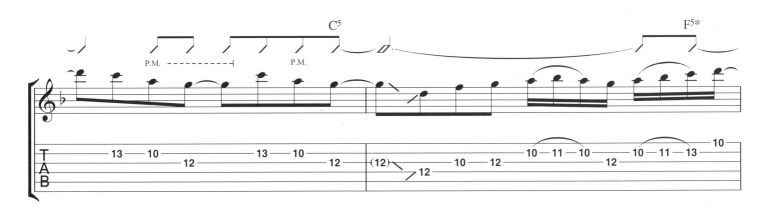

They are sealed _____ and are now _____ far a - way. _____

SCHOOL OF ROCK

WORDS & MUSIC BY MIKE WHITE & SAMMY JAMES, JR.

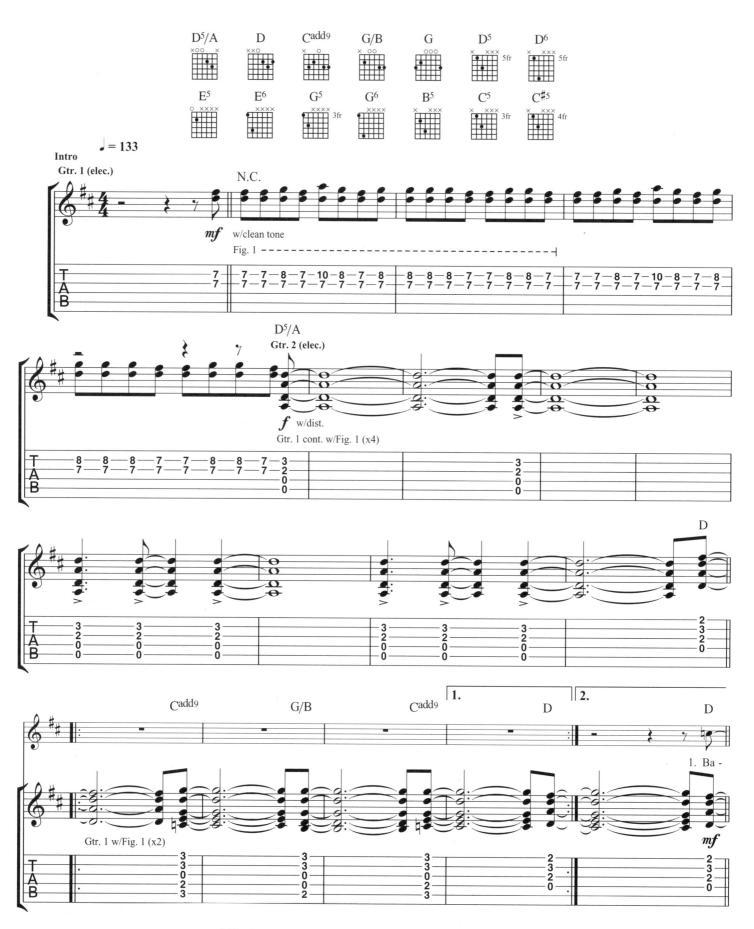

St. Anger

Words & Music by James Hetfield, Lars Ulrich, Kirk Hammett & Bob Rock

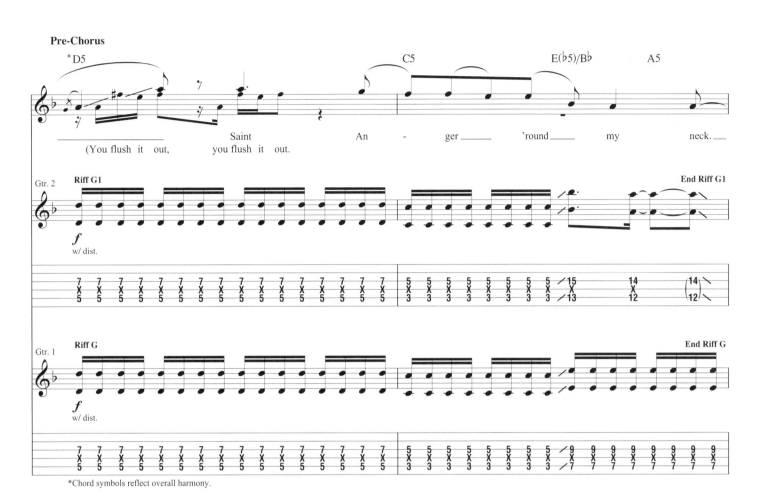

*Chord symbols reflect overall harmony.

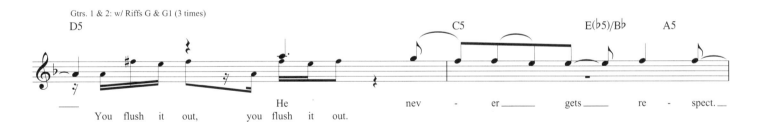

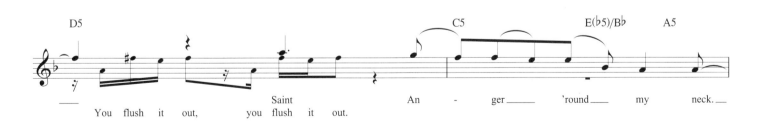

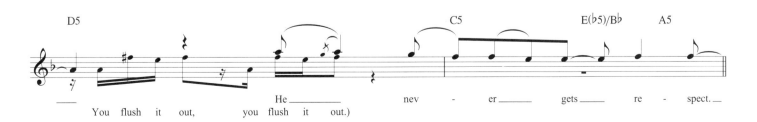

Interlude
Tempo I

Gtrs. 1 & 2: w/ Rhy. Figs. 1 & 1A

{ 1. *Voc. tacet* }
{ 2. Ooh! }

𝄋𝄋 Chorus
Double-time feel

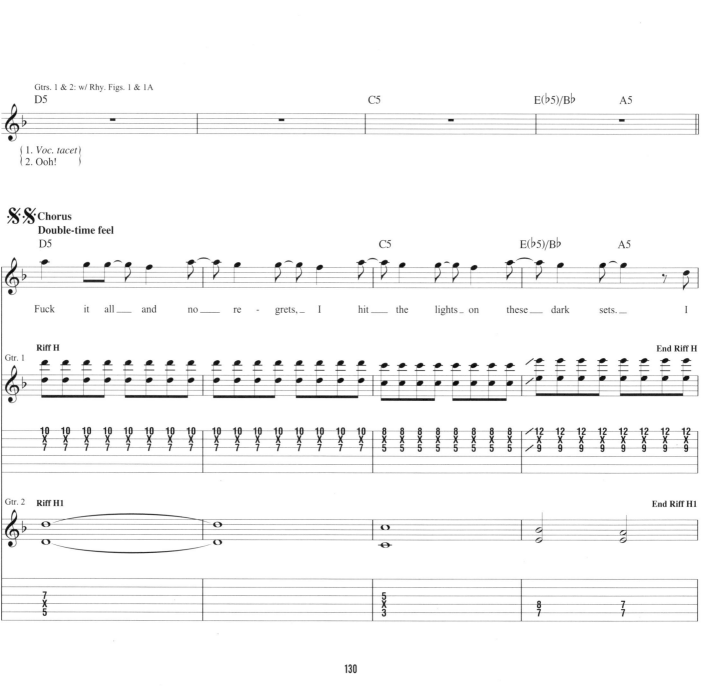

Fuck it all ___ and no ___ re - grets, I hit ___ the lights ___ on these ___ dark sets. ___ I

Interlude

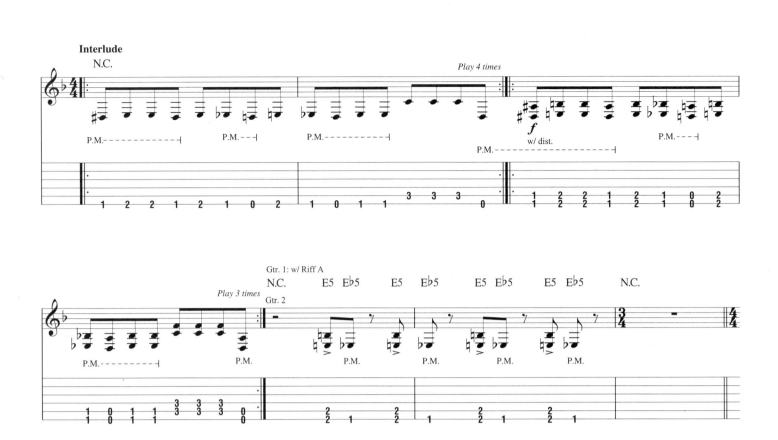

Gtr. 1: w/ Riff A

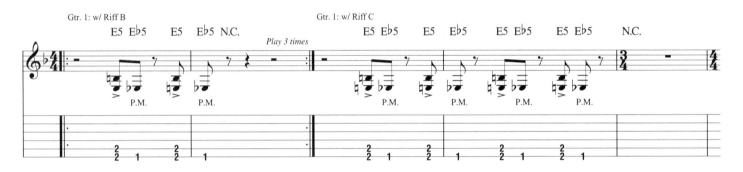

Gtr. 1: w/ Riff B   Gtr. 1: w/ Riff C

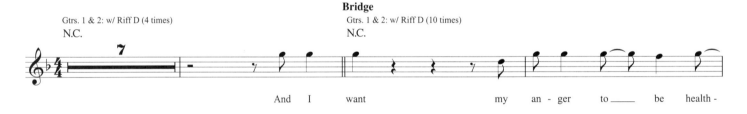

Bridge

Gtrs. 1 & 2: w/ Riff D (4 times)   Gtrs. 1 & 2: w/ Riff D (10 times)

And I want my an-ger to ___ be health-

- y. ___   And I want my an-ger just ___ for me. ___

___ And I need my an-ger not ___ to con-

- trol. ___   Yeah, ___ and I want my an-ger to ___ be me. ___

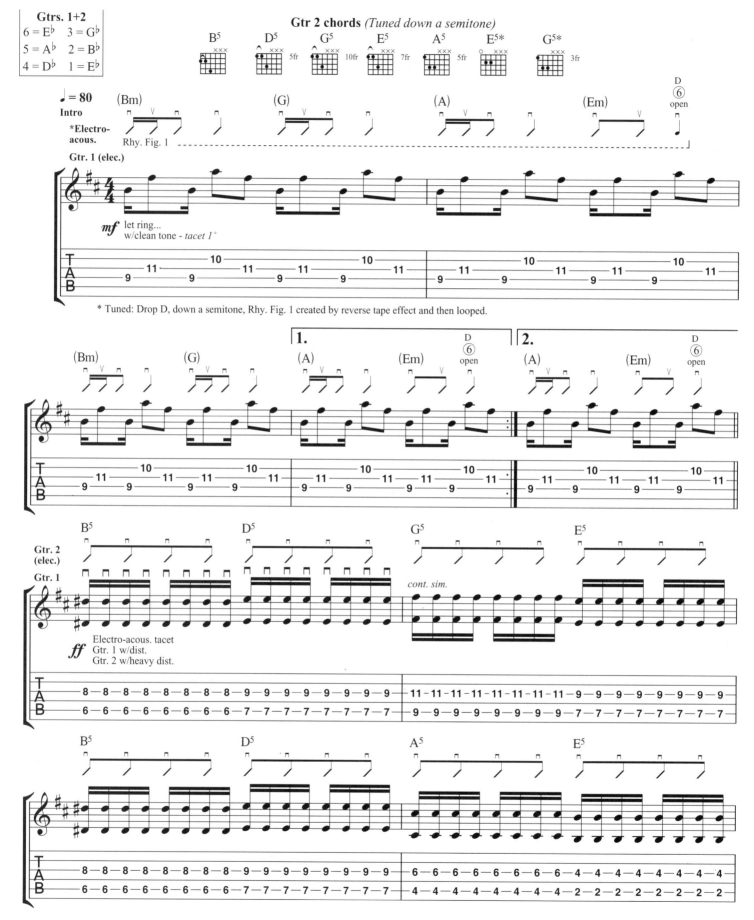

SOMEWHERE I BELONG

WORDS & MUSIC BY CHESTER BENNINGTON, ROB BOURDON, BRAD DELSON, JOSEPH HAHN, MIKE SHINODA & DAVID FARRELL

* Tuned: Drop D, down a semitone, Rhy. Fig. 1 created by reverse tape effect and then looped.

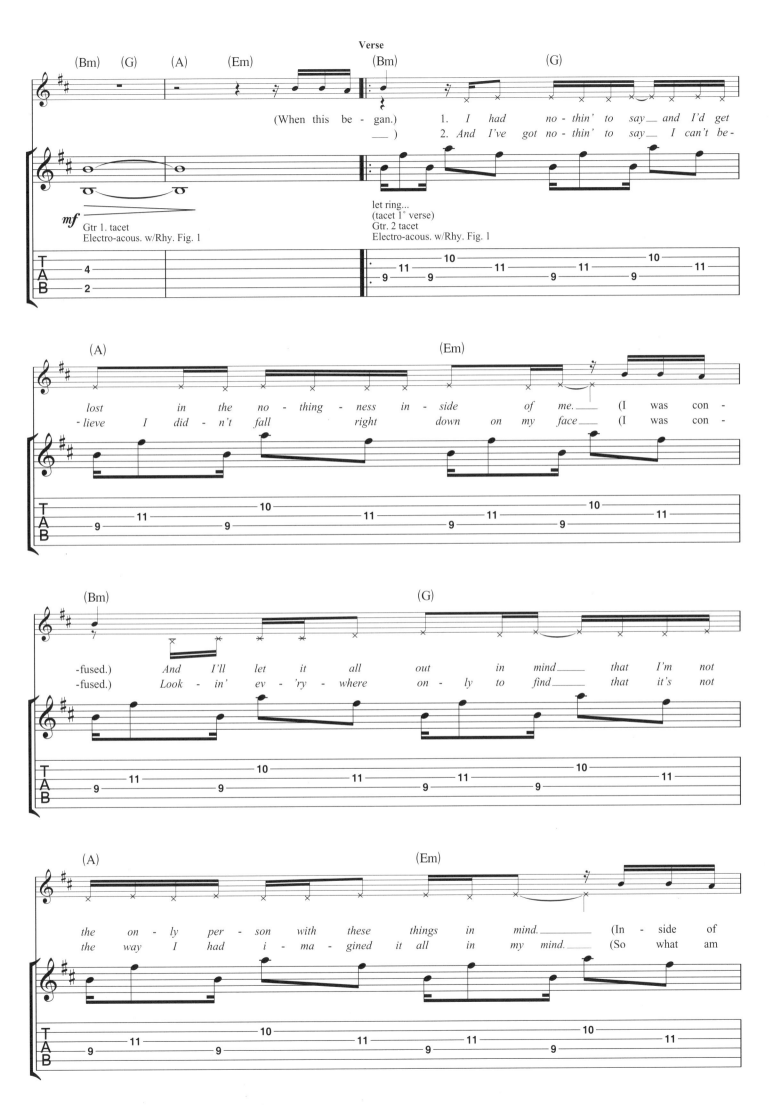

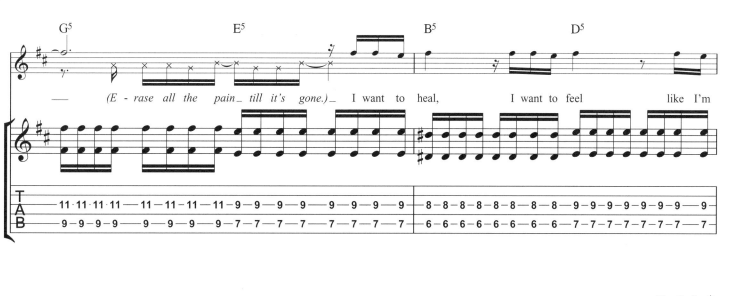

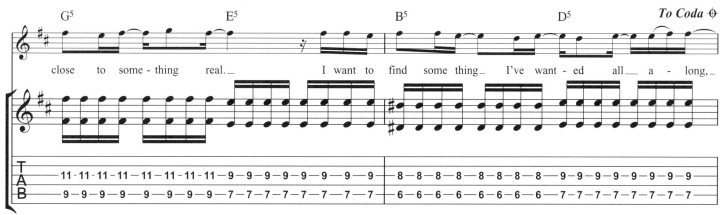

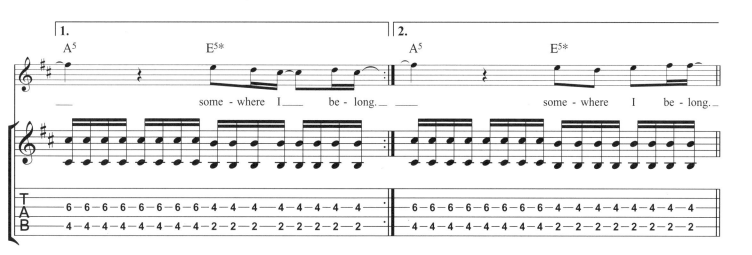

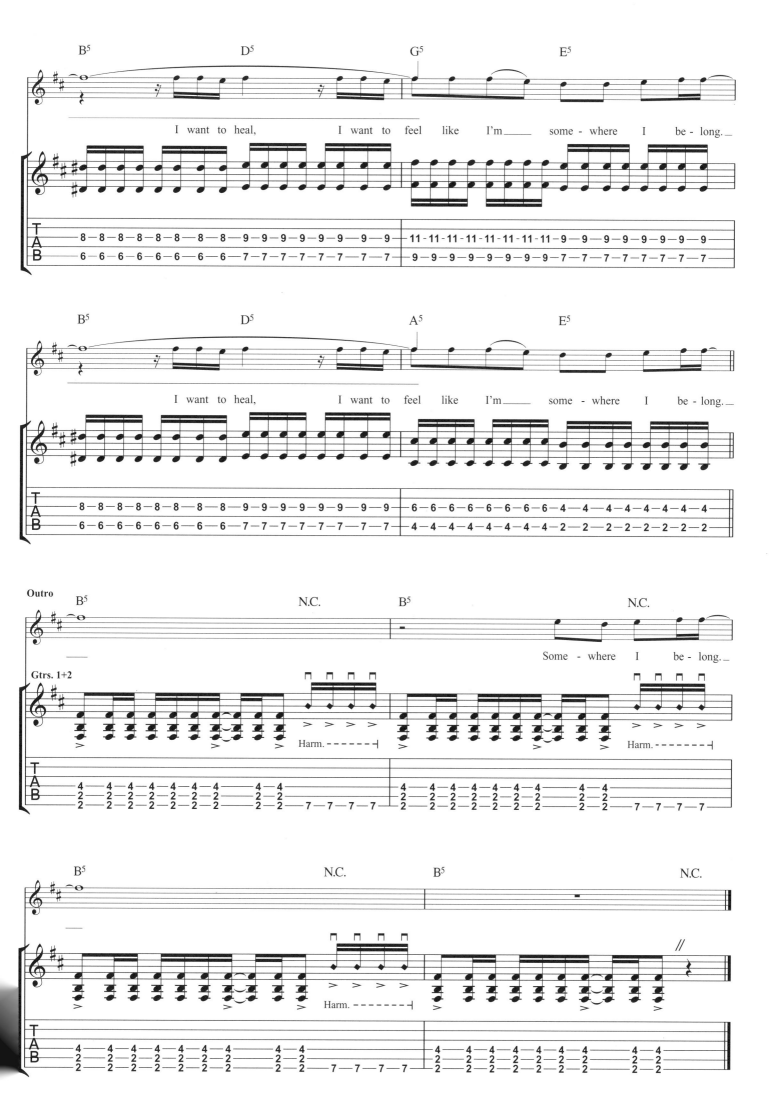

STOCKHOLM SYNDROME

WORDS & MUSIC BY MATTHEW BELLAMY, CHRIS WOLSTENHOLME & DOMINIC HOWARD

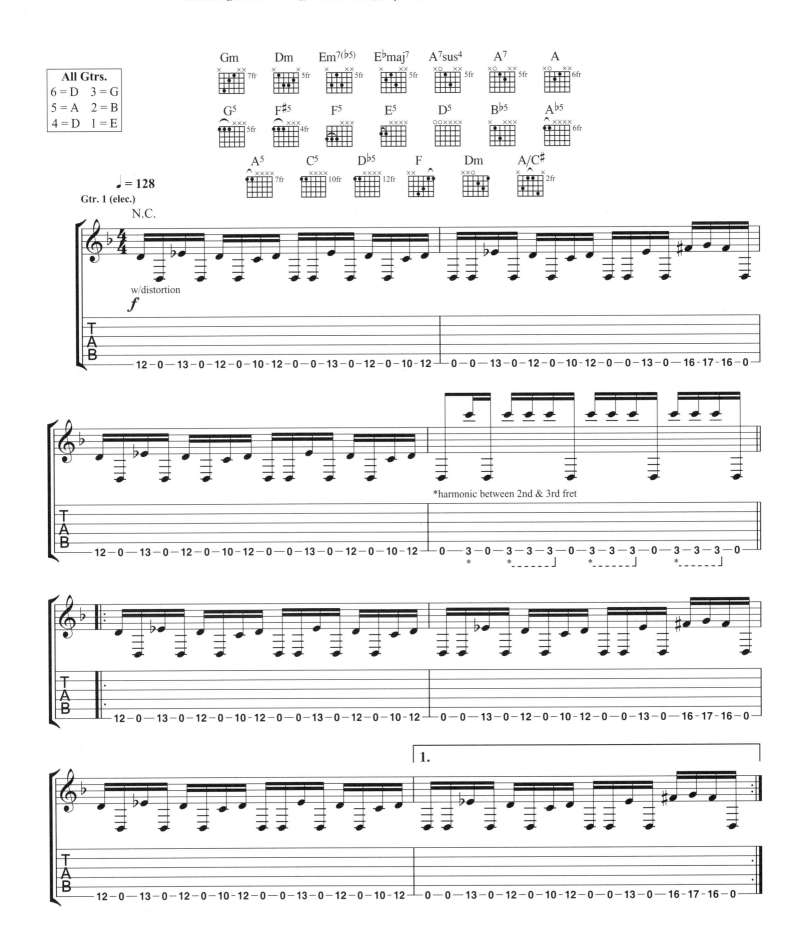

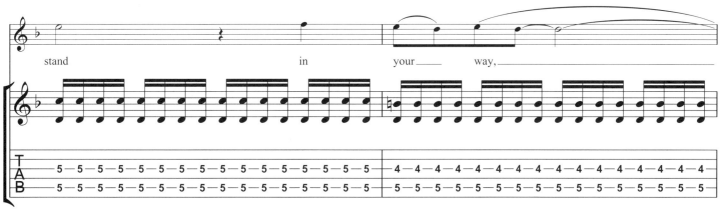

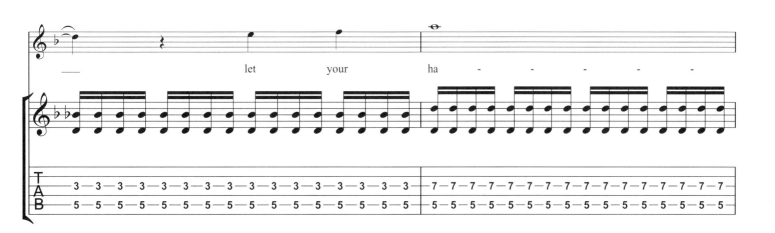

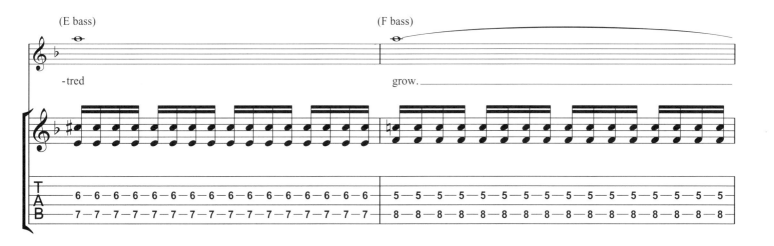

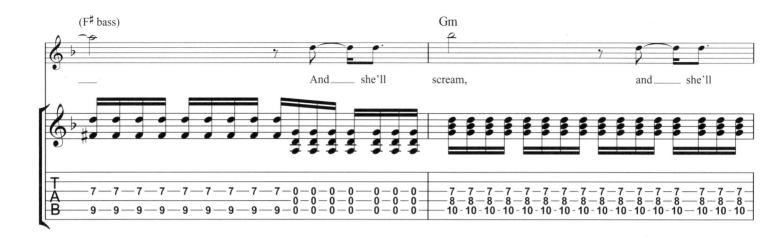

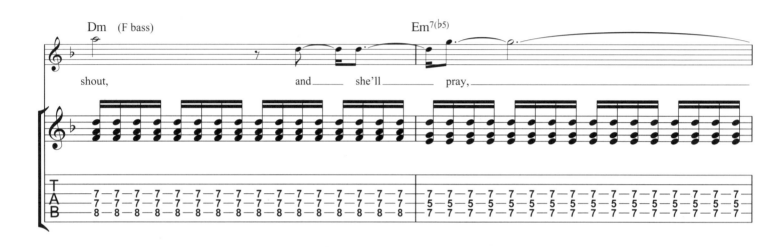

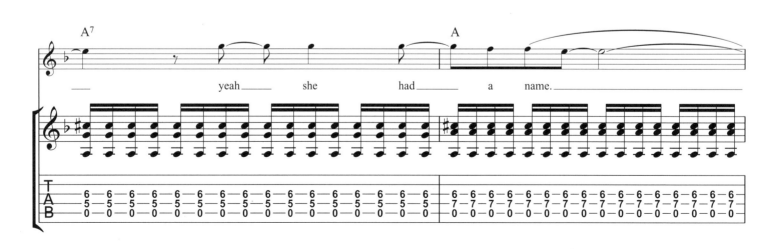

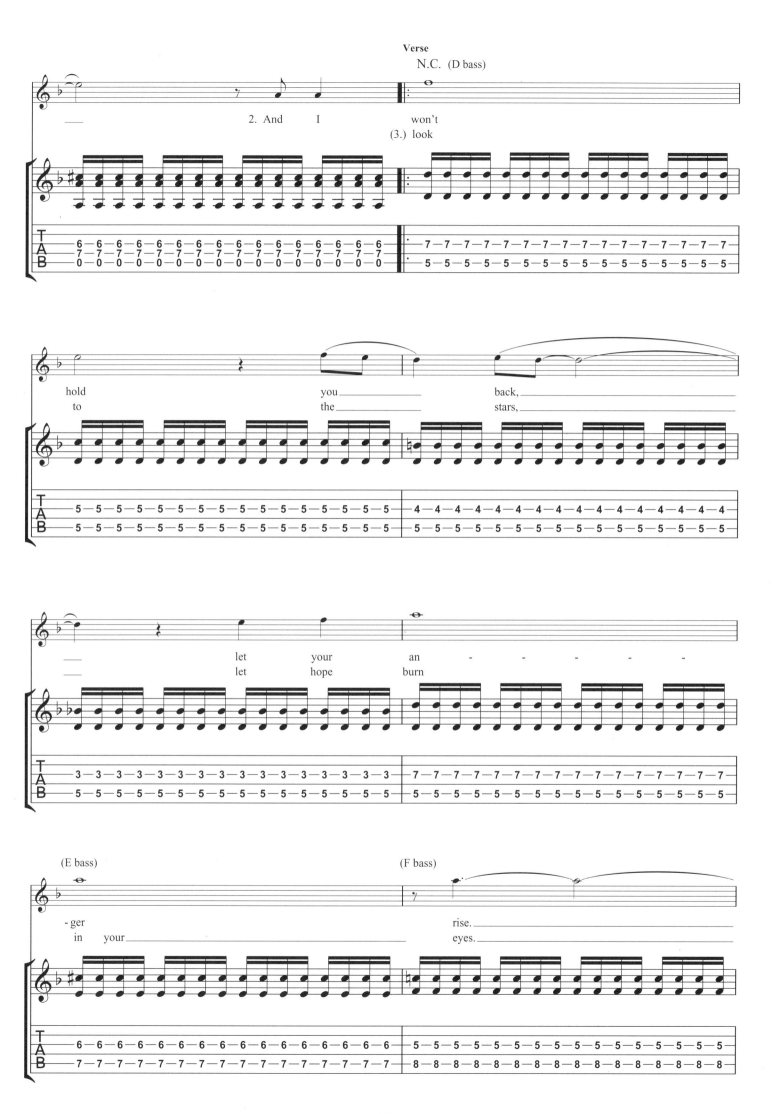

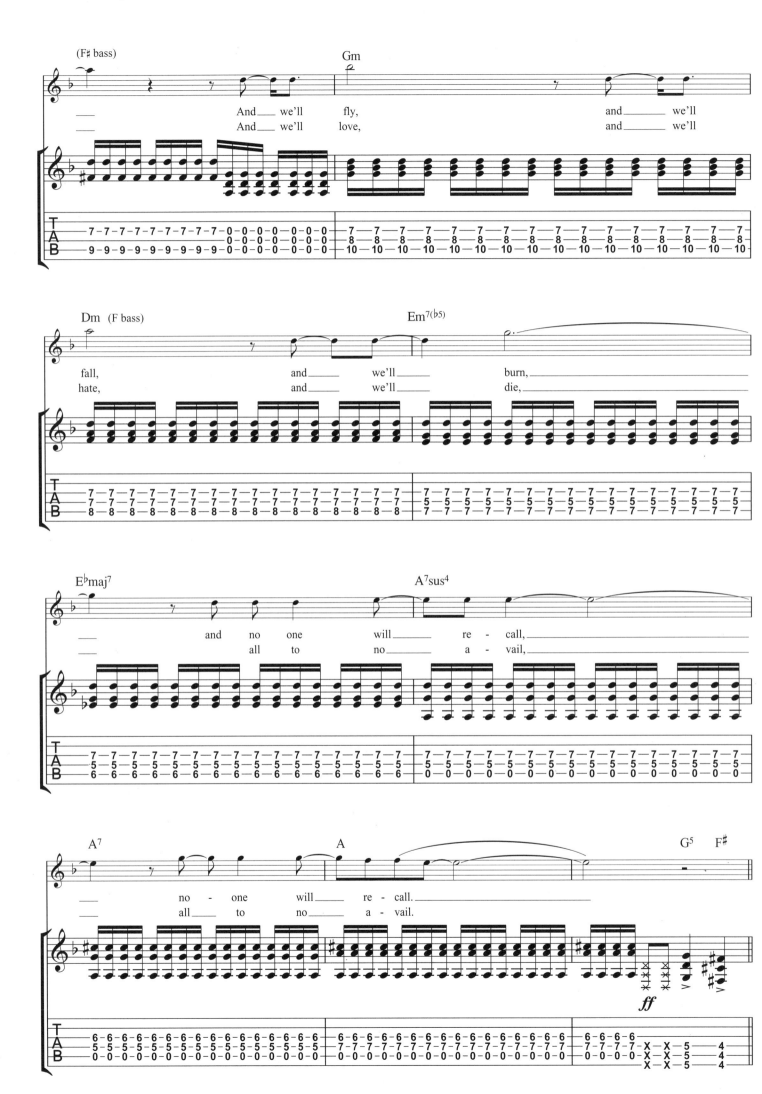

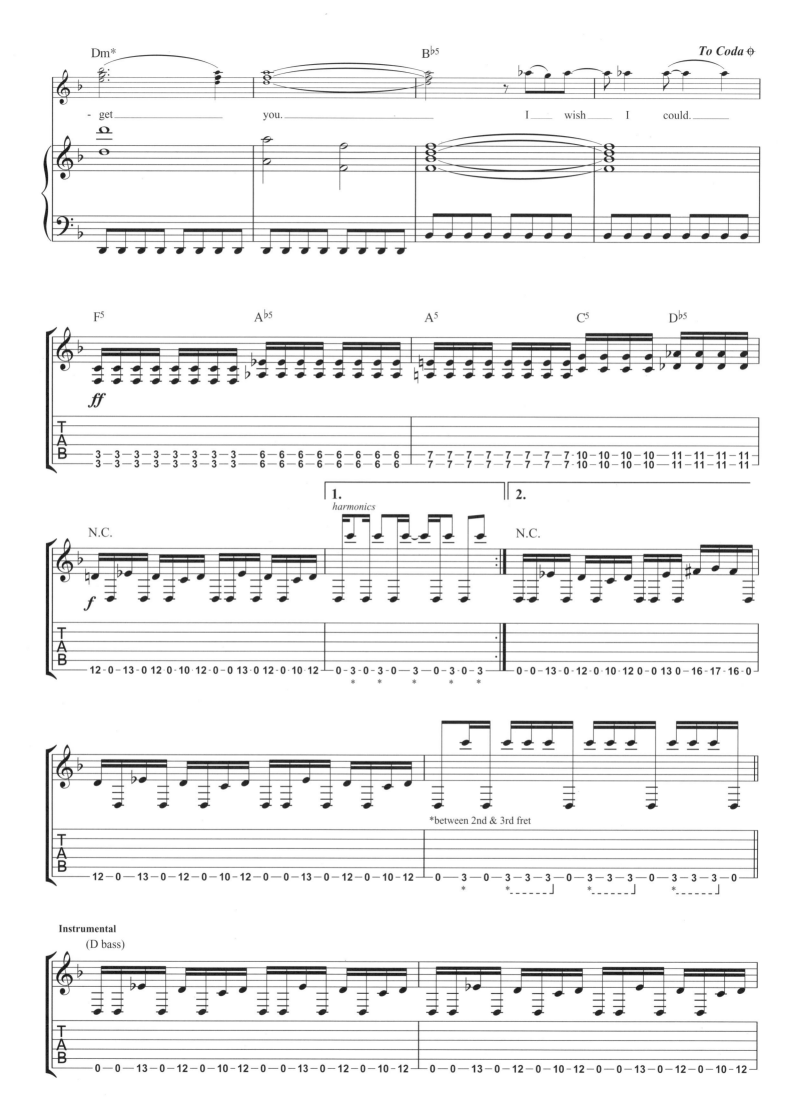

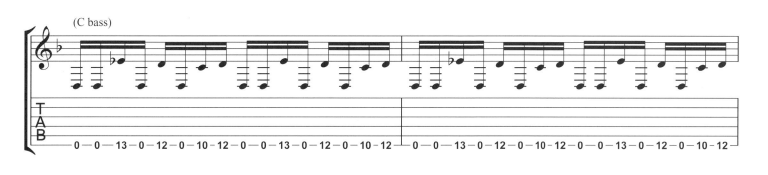

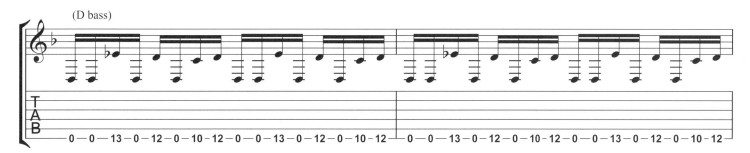

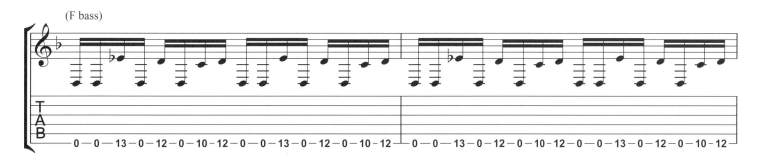

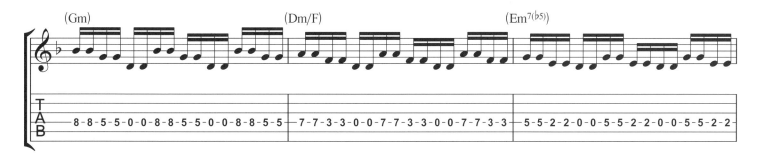

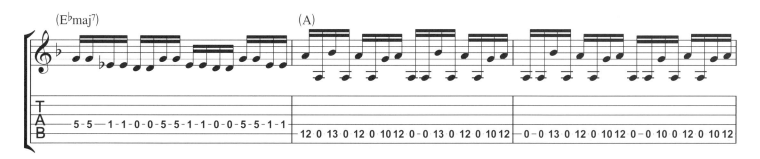

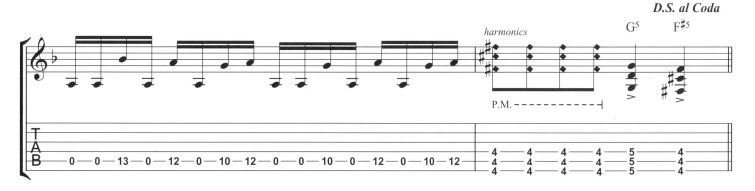

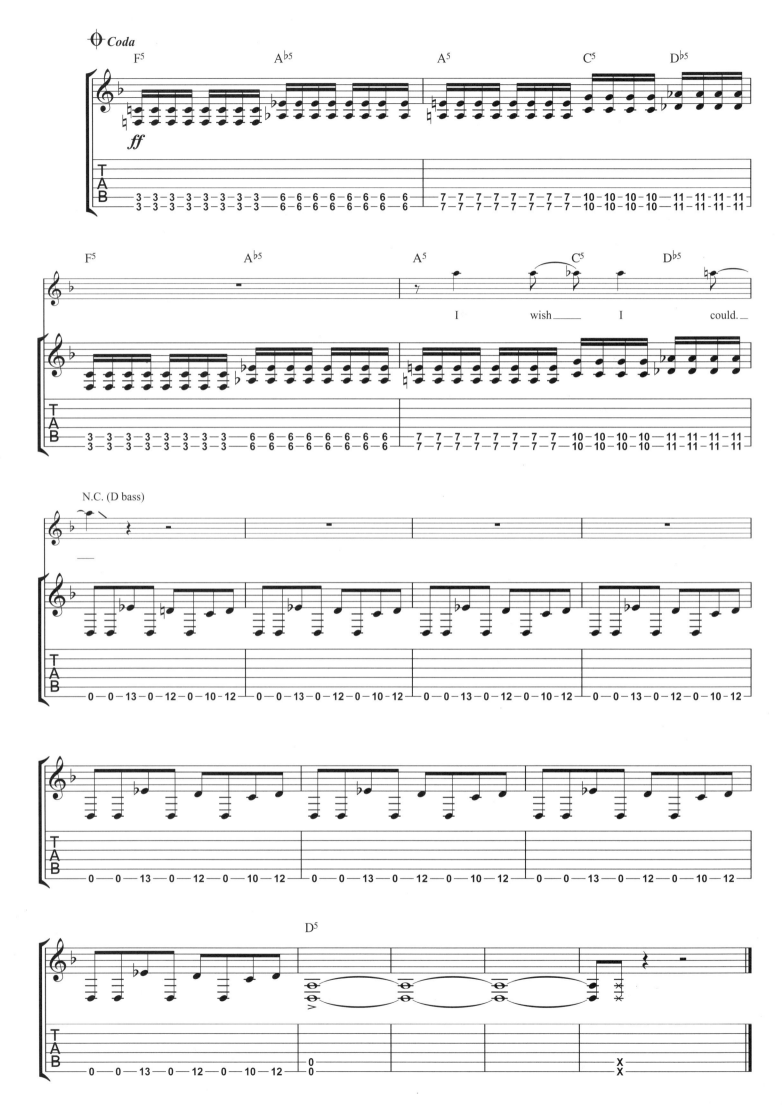

THIS IS IT
WORDS & MUSIC BY RYAN ADAMS & JOHNNY T. YERINGTON

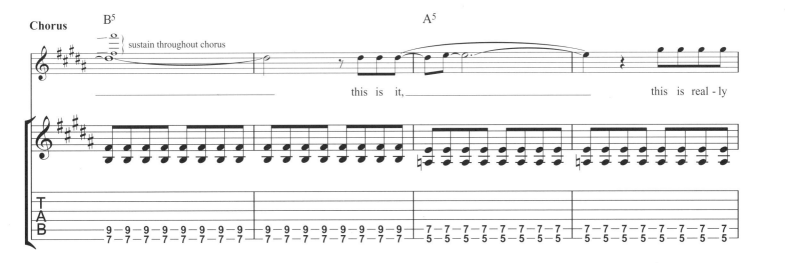

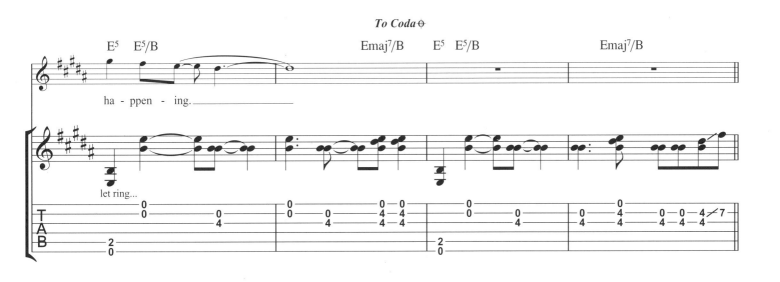

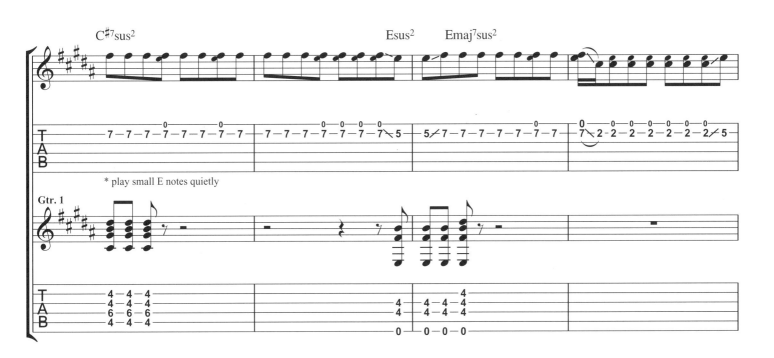

151

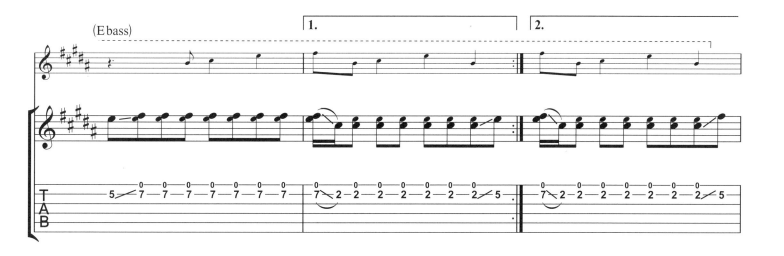

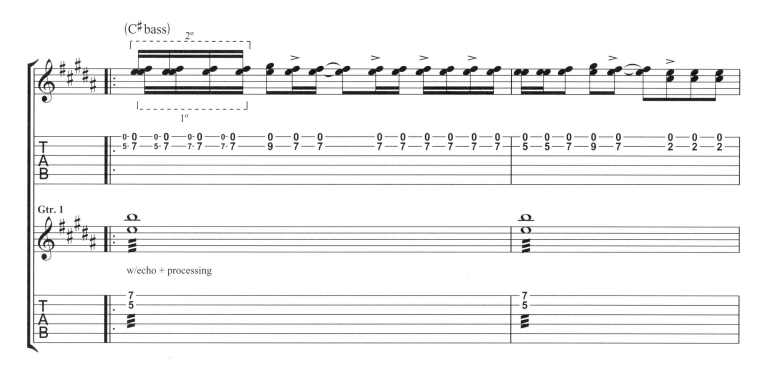

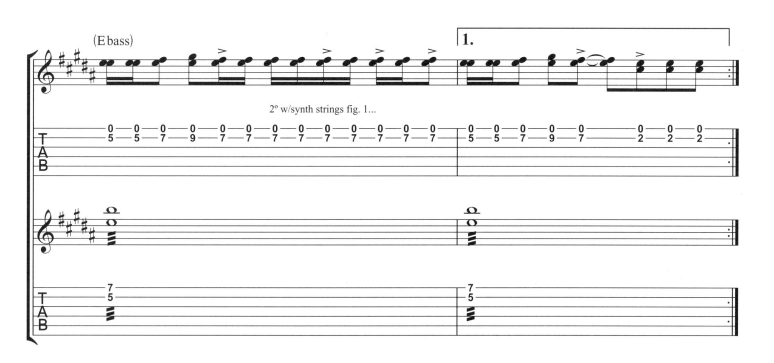

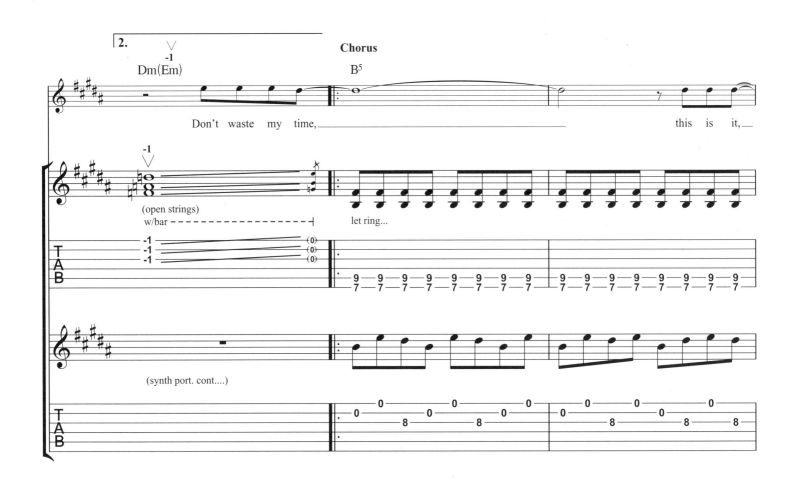

Don't waste my time,_____ this is it,___

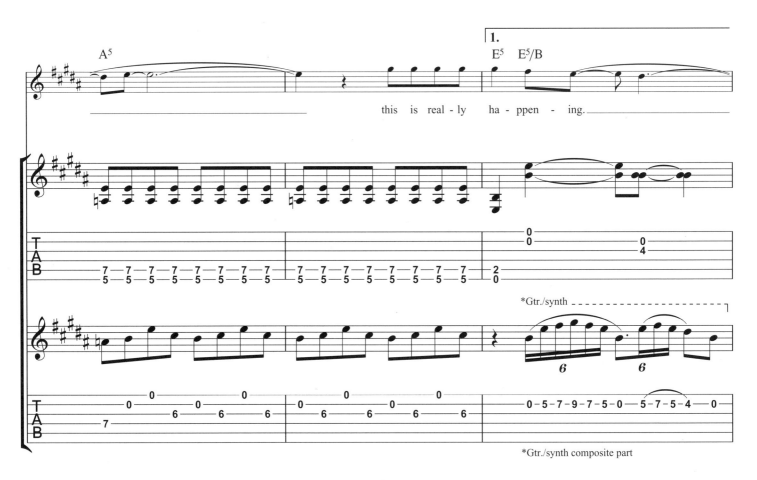

this is real-ly ha-ppen-ing._____

*Gtr./synth composite part

Times Like These

Words & Music by Dave Grohl, Taylor Hawkins, Nate Mendel & Chris Shiflett

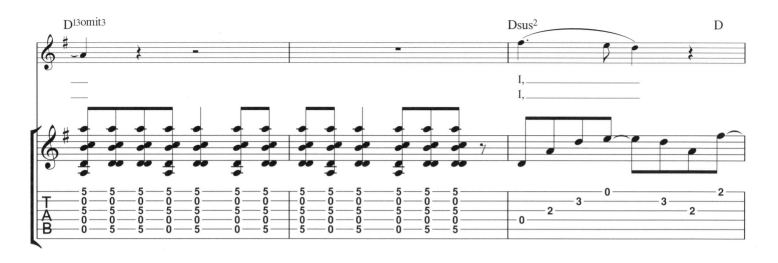

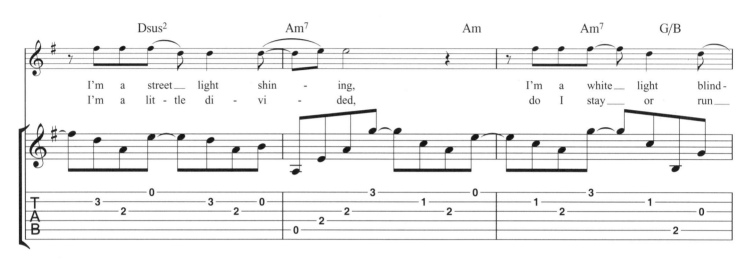

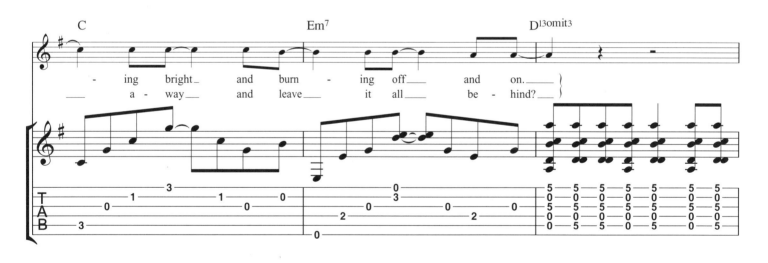

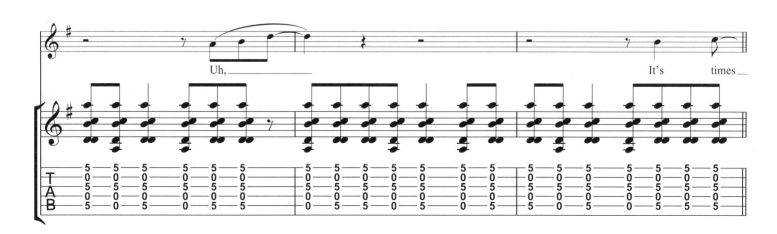

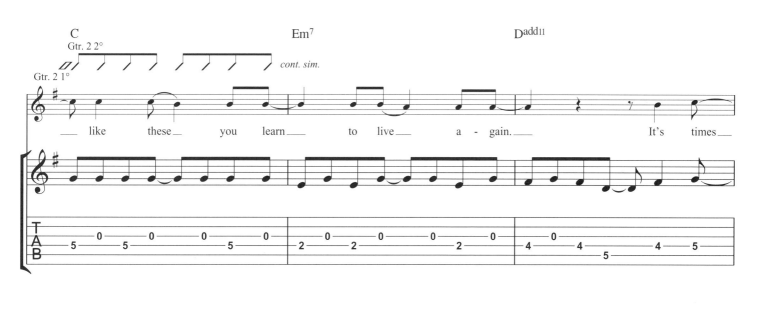

like these you learn to live a-gain. It's times

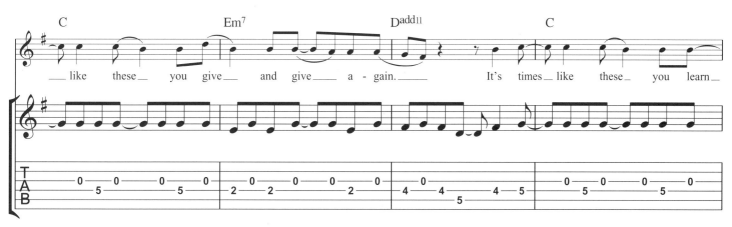

like these you give and give a-gain. It's times like these you learn

to love a-gain. It's times like these time and time a-gain.

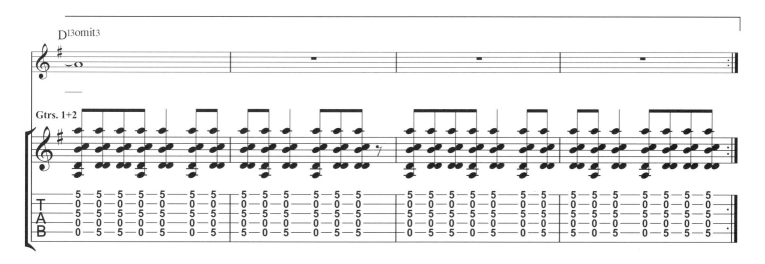

like these — you learn — to live a - gain. — It's times

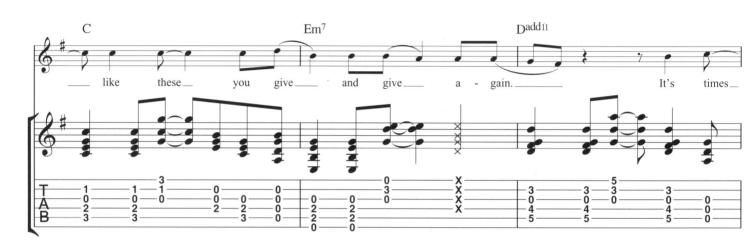

like these — you give — and give — a - gain. — It's times

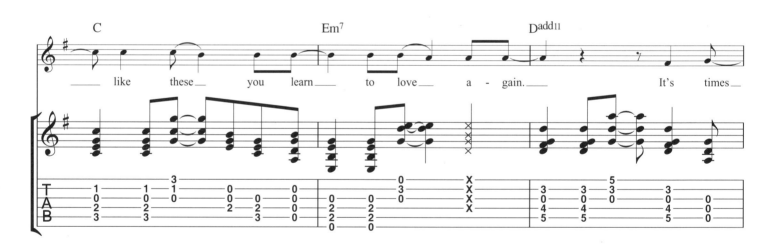

like these — you learn — to love — a - gain. — It's times

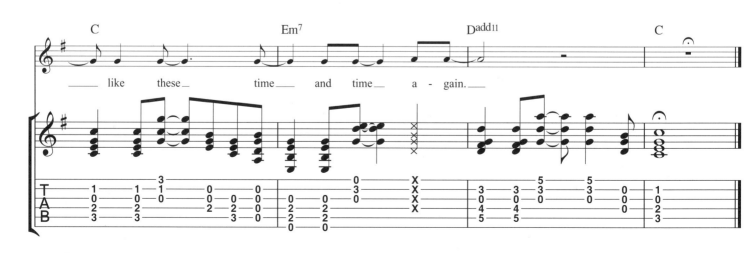

like these — time — and time — a - gain.

TRUE NATURE

WORDS & MUSIC BY PERRY FARRELL, DAVE NAVARRO, CHRIS CHANEY, STEPHEN PERKINS, MARTYN LENOBLE & BOB EZRIN

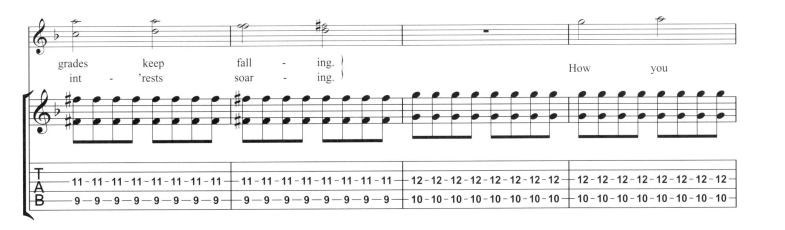

grades keep fall - ing.
int - 'rests soar - ing.

How you

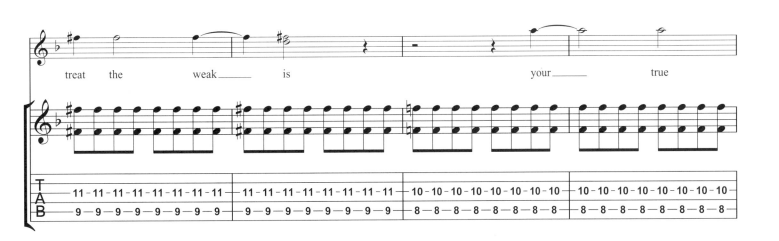

treat the weak_____ is

your_____ true

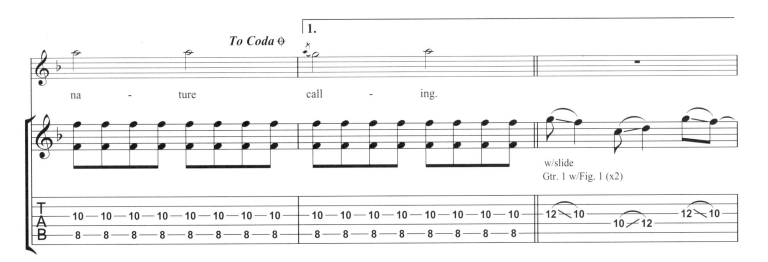

To Coda ⊕

1.

na - ture call - ing.

w/slide
Gtr. 1 w/Fig. 1 (x2)

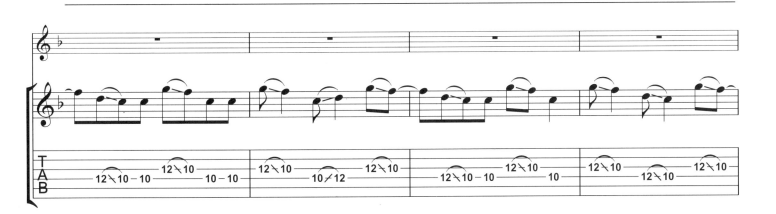

call - ing.

Gtr. 1 tacet

2.

Moth - er fuck - er, do you

1.

real - ly care?

2.

real - ly care?

Bridge

N.C. (B♭ bass)

Gtr. 3 (baritone gtr.) tuned C F B♭ E♭ G C

mf

Gtr. 1+2 tacet

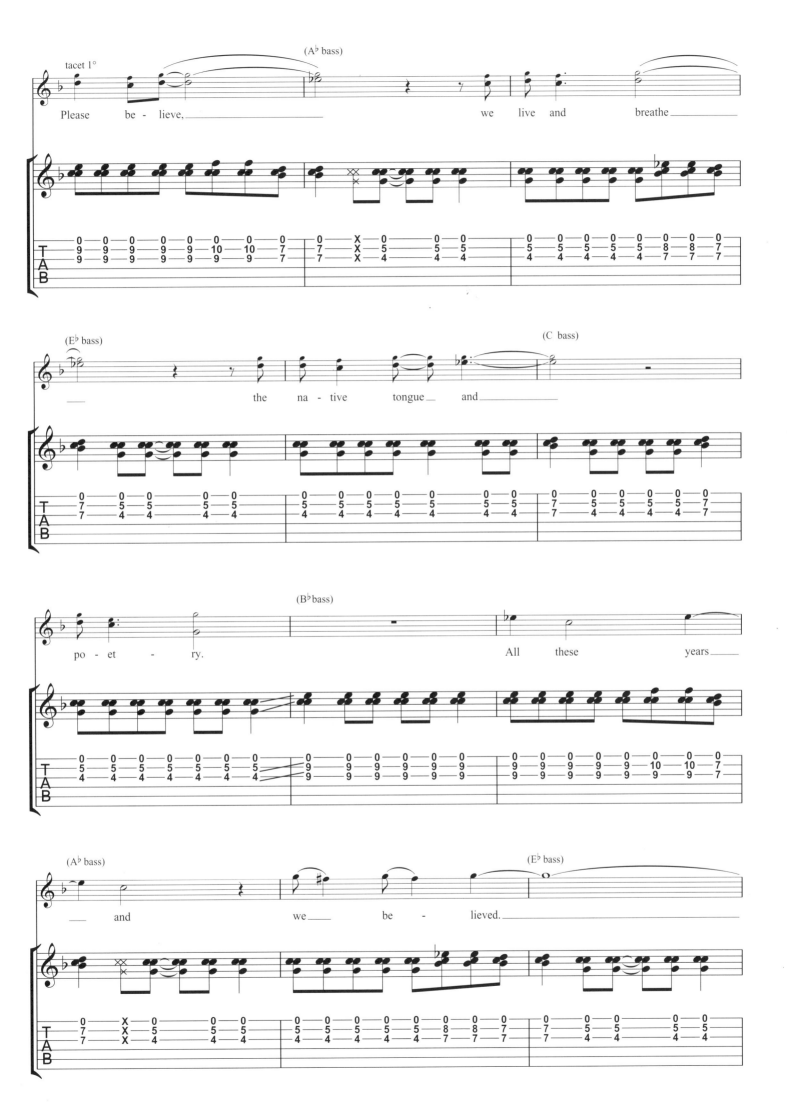

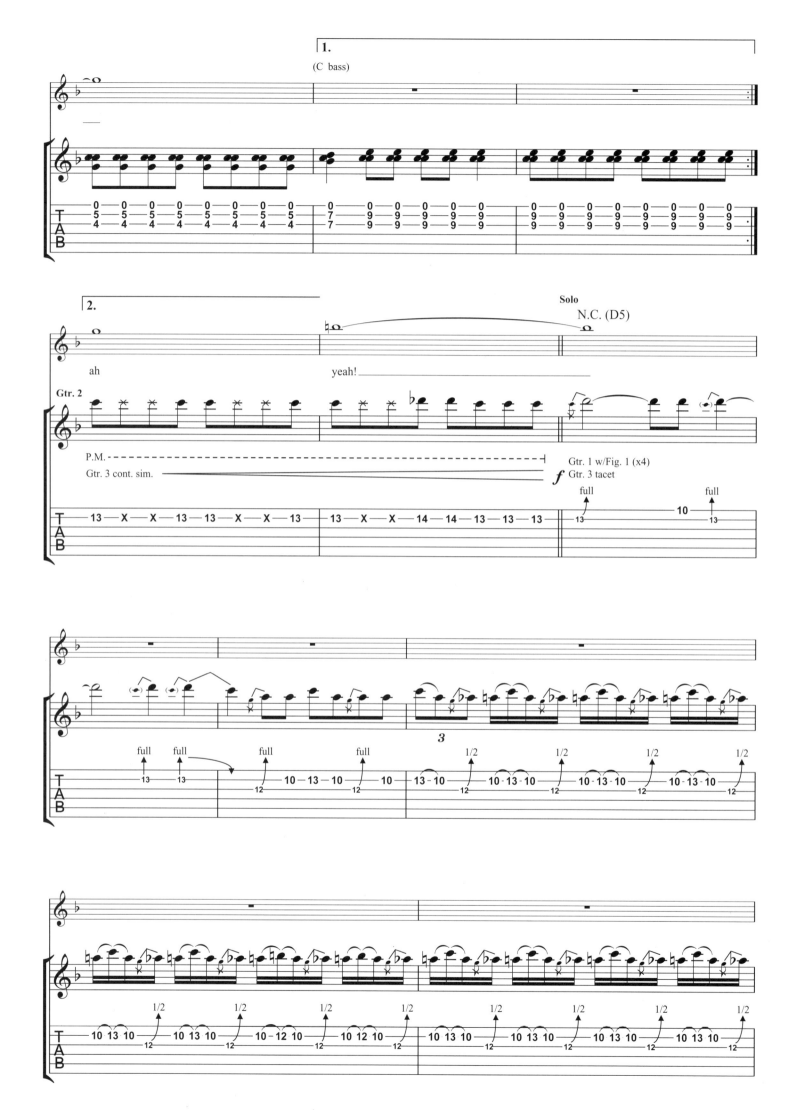

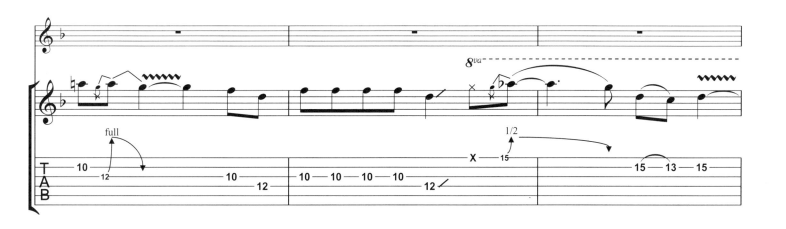

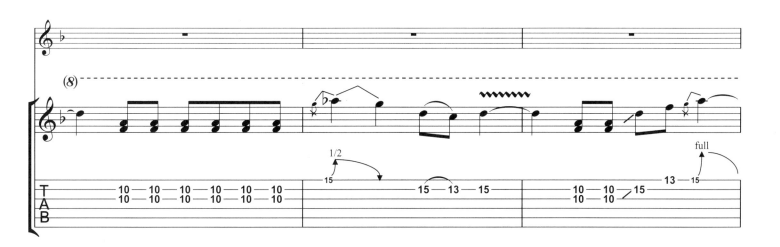

D.S. al Coda

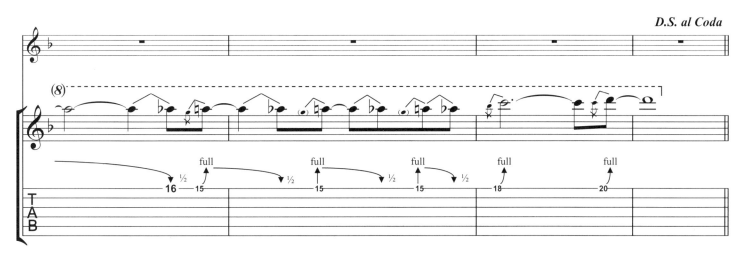

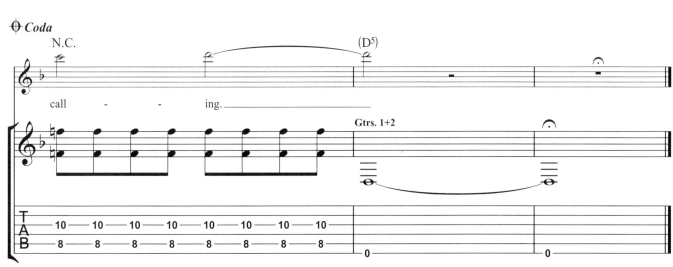

WASTED TIME

WORDS & MUSIC BY CALEB FOLLOWILL, NATHAN FOLLOWILL & ANGELO PETRAGLIA

right or wrong._ / out to night._

Oh take that ride,_ but_ I want your lit-tle sis-ter / Well it's O. K._ I know all_ a-bout the lit-tle

by your side,_ may-be lit-tle la-ter we can all col-lide, do our liv-ing like a / games you play_ sha-kin' your ap-ple right in my face,_ on-ly when you know that I'm

Pre-chorus

E⁵add♯11

Gtr. 2 *(2° only)*

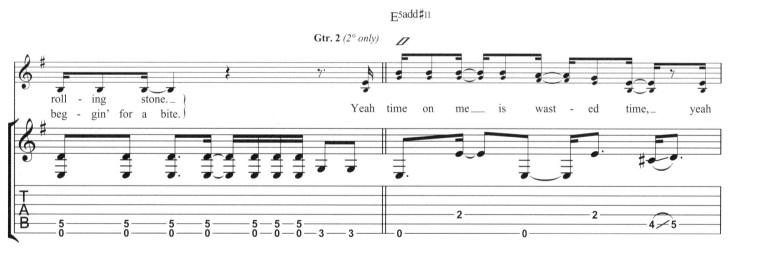

roll-ing stone._ } / beg-gin' for a bite. }

Yeah time on me_ is wast-ed time,_ yeah

time on me_ is wast-ed time,_ yeah time on me_ is wast-ed time,_ time on me_ is wast-ed.

I know the love you take - ah.

A - in - no - cent smile,__ a - run - nin' free.__

Ba - by gon - na give it like it used to be.__

Ba -

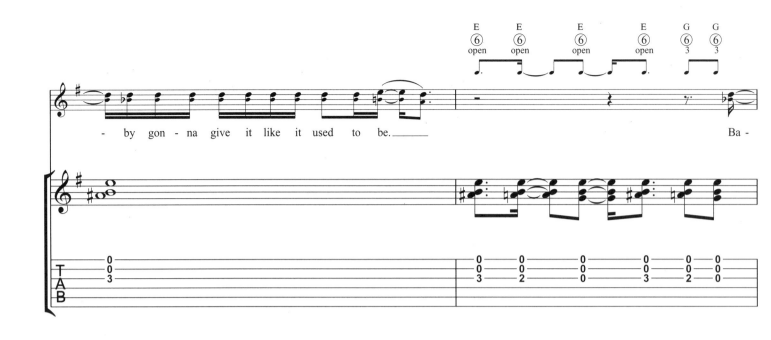

-by gon-na give it like it used to be._____ Ba-

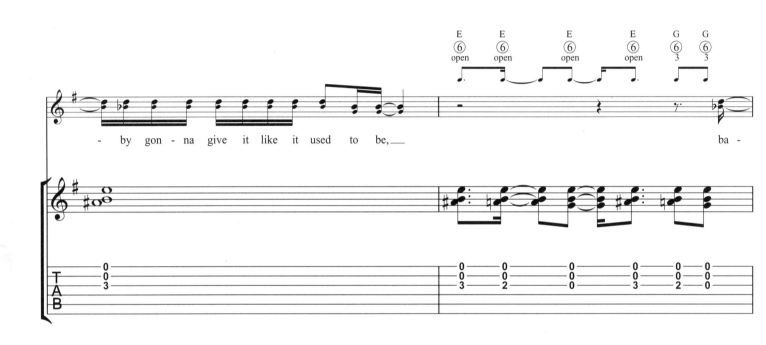

-by gon-na give it like it used to be,___ ba-

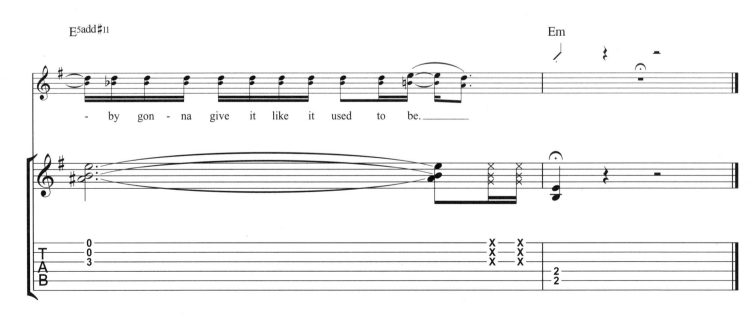

-by gon-na give it like it used to be._____